Reading Triumphs
INTERVENTION

Assessment

Program Authors

Dr. Jan E. Hasbrouck
Educational Consultant
J. H. Consulting
Seattle, Washington

Dr. Janice A. Dole
University of Utah
Salt Lake City, Utah

D1303451

 **Macmillan McGraw-Hill**

Published by Macmillan/McGraw-Hill,
of McGraw-Hill Education, a division of The McGraw-Hill Companies, Inc.,
Two Penn Plaza, New York, New York 10121.

Printed in the United States of America

5 6 7 8 9 10 021 10 09 08

Contents

Weekly and Unit Tests

Unit 1

Unit 2

Assessment Options

Assessment	Purpose	What It Does	When to Give It	How to Give It
Quick Phonics Screener	Diagnostic	Determine phonics instructional needs and placement in program's scope and sequence	Beginning, middle, and end of year	Administer individually
Letter Naming Fluency	Diagnostic	Determine students' mastery of letter names and sounds	Beginning, middle, and end of year (K–2 only)	Administer individually
Phoneme Segmentation Fluency	Diagnostic	Determine students' phonemic awareness skills	Beginning, middle, and end of year	Administer individually
Sight Word Fluency	Diagnostic	Determine students' mastery of basic high-frequency words	Beginning, middle, and end of year	Administer individually

Assessment	Purpose	What It Does	When to Give It	How to Give It
Timed Oral Fluency Reading	Progress Monitoring (Formative)	Determines if students are reading accurately and fluently	Once a unit	Administer individually
Leveled Text Reading	Progress Monitoring (Formative)	Determines instructional and independent reading levels	Once a unit	Administer individually
Weekly Assessment	Progress Monitoring (Formative)	Identifies students' strengths and weaknesses for instructional planning and grouping	At the end of a week of instruction	Whole group
Mid-Unit and End-of-Unit Assessments	Progress Monitoring (Formative)	Identifies students' strengths and weaknesses for instructional planning and grouping	After every 2 weeks (Mid-Unit) or 5 weeks (End-of-Unit) of instruction	Whole group

Entering the Program

The purpose of this handbook is to help you manage the use of multiple assessments, interpret the results, and then use that information for instructional planning. It will provide you with clear guidance on how test scores can be a useful resource for addressing your students' needs.

Macmillan/McGraw-Hill Triumphs Assessments

Our assessment options are …

- Grounded in research
- Compliant with the No Child Left Behind framework
- Based on studies of reliability and validity
- Aligned with standards
- Aligned with K–6 curriculum
- Easy to manage
- Designed to minimize testing time

District-Approved

Placing students in a formal intervention program is a high-stakes decision. It is recommended that you use your district-approved assessments to make this decision for each student. These may include the **TPRI** or **DIBELS** assessment.

TPRI (Texas Primary Reading Inventory)

Use for screening, diagnostic, and progress monitoring. These short probes measure Graphophonemic Knowledge and Phonemic Awareness (K–1) and Word Reading (1–3) and identify students not at risk of reading failure. The following are the diagnostic, or Inventory, subtests:

- **Book and Print Awareness (K)**
- **Phonemic Awareness (K–1)**
- **Listening Comprehension (K–1)**
- **Graphophonemic Knowledge (K–3)**
- **Reading Accuracy (1–3)**
- **Reading Fluency (1–3)**
- **Reading Comprehension (1–3)**

DIBELS (Dynamic Indicators of Basic Early Literacy Skills)

Use for screening and progress monitoring throughout the year. These are short, one-minute fluency measures that identify students as at risk, some risk, or low risk (or deficit, emerging, established). The probes measure all of the following:

- **Initial Sound Fluency (K)**
- **Phoneme Segmentation Fluency (K–1)**
- **Listening Comprehension (K–1)**
- **Oral Reading Fluency (1–3)**
- **Nonsense Word Fluency (K–3)**
- **Letter Naming Fluency (K–1)**
- **Reading Comprehension (1–3)**

Macmillan/McGraw-Hill Treasures Placement Test (Pre- and Post-Test)

The Treasures Placement Test can also be used. This test includes passages and items that assess comprehension, vocabulary, word recognition, phonics, and other skills. Students who achieve a total test score of 70%–90% should receive on-level reading instruction. Students who score higher than 90% should receive some beyond-level instruction. Students who score lower than 70% should receive approaching-level instruction. Students who show a pattern of low scores on this and other assessments should be evaluated for the Triumphs intervention program. This assessment should also be used as a Pre- and Post-Test to measure students' growth and readiness to enter the mainstream reading program.

Diagnostics

Once placement into the intervention program has been confirmed, use the following assessments to diagnose each student's individual skill needs.

- **Phonics Screener:** Determines which phonics skills students have mastered and can be used to place students within the program or to form small groups based on phonics needs.

- **Fluency Assessment:** This oral reading test determines how far below grade level students are, based on national norms. Since fluency and comprehension are highly correlated, this assessment is a key indicator of student progress and overall reading strength.

- **Comprehension (Leveled Passage) Test:** These leveled passages determine each student's instructional and independent reading levels and are sensitive to reading growth.

Progress Monitoring

What Is a Progress Monitoring Assessment?

- An informal or formal assessment used to guide instruction.

- A test that is usually quick and easy to administer and score.

- A test that is given individually or in a group.

- A test that is administered frequently: every week, every two weeks, or every five or six weeks, depending on which specific test you select.

- A test that is both systematic and ongoing, with results that are documented and recorded.

How to Use the Results

- Use the results to help guide instructional decision-making.

- These are formative assessments; they provide real information, not just scores or grades. The information should be used to plan future instruction.

- Use the results to provide feedback to students on how they are progressing. This feedback can take the form of written and oral comments related to specific skills, or an analysis of a student's strengths and weaknesses.

Informal Observation

QuickChecks

Triumphs provides many opportunities for you to observe students independently practice a strategy or skill taught.

• The **QuickChecks** remind you to observe your students and see if any of them are having difficulty with a skill they just learned.

• You can use this information to decide if this is a skill you need to address in small-group instruction.

Corrective Feedback

Feedback is a key part of assessment. Feedback should help students see how they can improve their work. The most useful feedback is a specific comment describing the strengths and weaknesses of individual work, with useful suggestions for improvement. Corrective feedback may also consist of showing the child another way to understand the skill, by breaking the skill down into its components to aid in understanding.

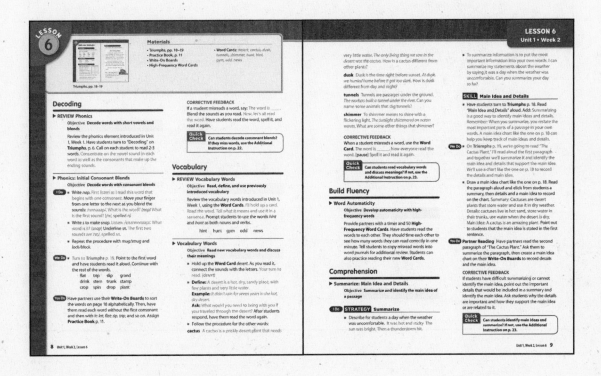

Weekly Tests

The **Weekly Assessment** is designed to assess your students' mastery of the skills taught throughout the week. Each week there will be a new passage for students to read. The test questions cover comprehension, vocabulary, and decoding strategies and skills. Use the results of the Weekly Assessment as a formative assessment tool to help monitor student progress. Information gathered by evaluating the results of this assessment can also be used to diagnose specific strengths and weaknesses of your students.

Mid-Unit and End-of-Unit Tests

The **Mid-Unit Assessment** (given in Week 2 of each unit) and the **End-of-Unit Assessment** (given in Week 5 of each unit) is a cumulative test focusing on the skills taught throughout the unit. These assessments are formative. Evaluate the results to diagnose students' strengths and weaknesses. Scores that fall below 80% suggest that students require additional instruction.

At a Coral Reef

It was Jeff's first time swimming at a coral reef. He was so excited! This year, his class's annual trip was a visit to Mexico. The trip would have been too expensive for Jeff's family. But the school was offered a special package rate. Jeff felt as if he had been given a wonderful present all tied up in beautiful wrapping. On the plane, he was so excited he kept walking up and down the aisles. The flight attendant asked him politely to sit down. This trip had the potential to be one he would never forget.

Jeff swam over the reef. He was surprised at how warm the water was. He lived in Maine. There, the ocean was almost always cold. He never went swimming in winter. He thought it was like that everywhere. But it was February, and here in Mexico the water was warm!

It was hard to believe this was all real. Jeff had never seen so many brightly colored fish in one place. And the coral was just as pretty. In some places it was even more colorful than the fish.

Before the trip, Jeff had read books about coral. He learned that most coral is brittle. Rough waves can break it. Jeff knew there were certain things that he was not supposed to do. The other students did not know this. Jeff knew never to stand on coral. That could hurt it. He learned never to take live coral out of the water. That can kill it. He also learned that he never should touch living coral. He could get hurt touching it.

Jeff was glad he had learned about coral before coming here. Now he would not make an innocent mistake that might hurt the coral or hurt him. He could spend all of his time enjoying the fish and the reef!

Name _____

Directions: Fill in the circle next to the best answer.

1. **What is the meaning of the underlined word in the sentence below?**

   The <u>wrapping</u> on the present Jeff got had pictures of fish on it.

   Ⓐ knock
   Ⓑ paper, plastic, or cloth used to cover something
   Ⓒ to speak freely
   Ⓓ to cover

2. **What does *annual* mean in the sentence below?**

   This year, the <u>annual</u> class trip is a visit to Canada.

   Ⓐ daily
   Ⓑ weekly
   Ⓒ yearly
   Ⓓ rarely

3. **Choose the word that completes the sentence below.**

   Please do not run in the _____ of the plane.

   Ⓐ isle
   Ⓑ aisle
   Ⓒ I'll
   Ⓓ ill

Phonics Screener

The **QPS** (Quick Phonics Screener) assessment, developed by Dr. Jan Hasbrouck, determines each student's decoding strengths and weaknesses. The assessment is coded so that each skill can be linked to the grade in which instruction and mastery is expected. This assessment will help form small groups and place students in the program.

Fluency

The **Fluency Assessment** consists of passages and fluency record sheets to help you record oral reading accuracy and important aspects of oral reading fluency. The assessments will tell you how many words a student can read aloud per minute and how many of these words are read correctly. Information gathered from the Fluency Record Sheet may be used to verify or clarify instructional decisions. Oral Reading accuracy is a percentage score based on the total number of words read and the number of errors noted. If a student's words correct per minute falls more than ten points below the benchmarks for that grade, the student is not reading fluently. The goal is for a student to be reading at the 50th percentile for his/her grade level on a grade-appropriate passage.

Leveled Passages

The **Leveled Passage Test** consists of a series of graded passages (one per grade). Students begin reading the passage 2 or more years below their expected reading level. They then read until their instructional level is determined. This assessment can be used to determine when students are ready to receive grade-level reading instruction and to make decisions about independent reading.

Exiting the Program

Based on your informal observations and students' weekly and unit assessments, determine those students who are ready to transition into the mainstream basal reading program. Use the assessments below to confirm students' preparedness to handle grade-level or approaching grade-level work.

- **Phonics:** Use the QPS (Quick Phonics Screener) to determine if the student's decoding skills are approaching grade-level expectations.

- **Fluency:** Use the Oral Reading Fluency test to determine if the student's fluency rate is approaching grade-level norms.

- **Comprehension:** Use the Leveled Passage Test to determine if student's instructional reading level is at or near grade-level.

- **Placement Tests:** Use the Treasures Placement Test as a Post-Test to measure the student's reading growth.

Step-by-Step Transition from Intervention to On-Level Reading Instruction			
Strand	**TRIUMPHS** Intervention Program	**APPROACHING LEVEL** in Treasures and/or appropriate leveled books	**ON-LEVEL** Reading Instruction (Treasures or other basal series)
Phonics	Tasks 1–9 Below 80% correct on one or more tasks	Tasks 1–9 80% or higher correct on all tasks	Tasks 1–10 80% or higher correct on all tasks
Fluency	Fall 1–43 wcpm Winter 1–61 wcpm Spring 1–77 wcpm	Fall 44–70 wcpm Winter 62–91 wcpm Spring 78–106 wcpm	Fall 71+ wcpm Winter 92+ wcpm Spring 107+ wcpm
Comprehension	Grade 1 passage	Grade 2 passage	Grade 3 passage

Phonics (Quick Phonics Screener)

- Contains real and nonsense words

- Connected to grade-level in which skills are taught

- Measures growth in basic decoding skills

- Ideal for diagnosis of specific skill needs and placement

Quick Phonics Screener - Standard Version

Task 1(a)	m	t	a	s	i	r	d	f	o
	g	l	h	u	c	n	b	j	k
Task 1(b)	y	e	w	p	v	qu	x	z	

| Task 2(a) | wat | fod | leb | tum | pon |
| | sib | cug | raf | mip | hev |

Task 2(b)	Sam and Ben hid the gum.
	Pat had a nap in bed.
	Mom had a top on a big pot.
	Tim can sit in a tub.

| Task 3(a) | shap | ming | gack | whum | pith |
| | chan | thog | kosh | mich | whaf |

| Task 3(b) | That duck had a wet wing. | Brad hit a log with a whip. |
| | When can Chip pack? | A fish is in that tub. |

| Task 4(a) | clab | trin | snaf | greb | slad |
| | fosp | lonk | mant | jast | sund |

| Task 4(b) | Glen will swim past the raft in the pond. |
| | The frog must flip and spin and jump. |

| Task 5(a) | sice | nole | fune | moze | vate |
| | rine | lade | sile | gane | fote |

| Task 5(b) | Mike and Jane use a rope to ride the mule. |
| | Pete had five tapes at home. |

© Macmillan/McGraw-Hill

22   Phonics Assessment

Quick Phonics Screener - Standard Version

© Macmillan/McGraw-Hill

| Task 6(a) | cort | pirk | varb | serl | surd |
| | tarn | forp | murk | tim | kerm |

| Task 6(b) | The tar on his torn shirt burned and hurt him. |
| | The bird hid under the short ferns in the park. |

| Task 7(a) | litch | mudge | glux | quam | celp |
| | gerb | knaz | gnap | wrill | ralk |

Task 7(b)	The cider is in the wrong cup.
	She ran to the center of the bridge.
	I will stitch a knot on the quilt.
	The giant can gnaw on the box.

Task 8	foat	roast	frea	creak	moom	scoop	raim	waist
	folt	scold	dray	gray	chout	mount	poid	join
	moy	royal	vaul	fault	praw	straw	koe	toe
	frew	jewel	palk	scald	pigh	fight		

| Task 9(a) | mascot | basket | moment | bacon | handle |
| | puzzle | cartoon | order | escape | chowder |

| Task 9(b) | amputate | liberty | dominate | elastic | entertain |
| | practical | innocent | electric | volcano | segregate |

| Task 9(c) | particular | contaminate | community | superior | vitality |
| | evaporate | inventory | prehistoric | solitary | emergency |

Task 10	discount	dismiss	nonsense	nostop	index	intent
	prefix	prepare	return	regard	unable	uncertain
	confident	concert	station	motion	famous	joyous
	madness	witness	portable	drinkable	fastest	dampest
	mouthful	fearful	honorary	literary	instrument	fragment

Phonics Assessment   23

Below Level	**Approaching Level**	**On Level**
Tasks 1–9	Tasks 1–9	Tasks 1–10
Below 80% correct on one or more tasks	80% or higher correct on all tasks	80% or higher correct on all tasks

© Macmillan/McGraw-Hill

Fluency

- Measures oral reading

- Linked to national norms

- Highly correlated to a student's comprehension of grade-level text

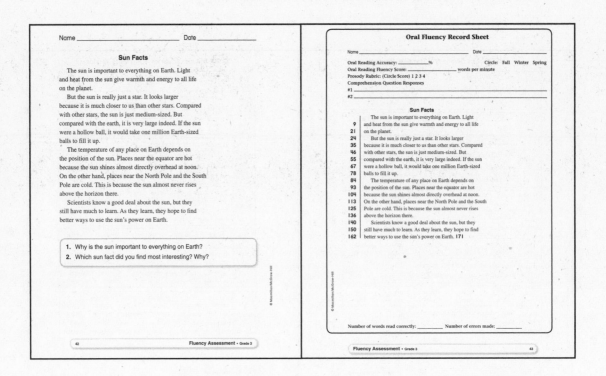

	Below Level	Approaching Level	On Level
Fall	1–43 wcpm	44–70 wcpm	71+ wcpm
Winter	1–61 wcpm	62–91 wcpm	92+ wcpm
Spring	1–77 wcpm	78–106 wcpm	107+ wcpm

*Prosody Level score of 3 or 4

Assessment • Exiting the Program

Comprehension

- Leveled text reading

- Shows reading growth over time

- Indicates student's independent and instructional reading levels

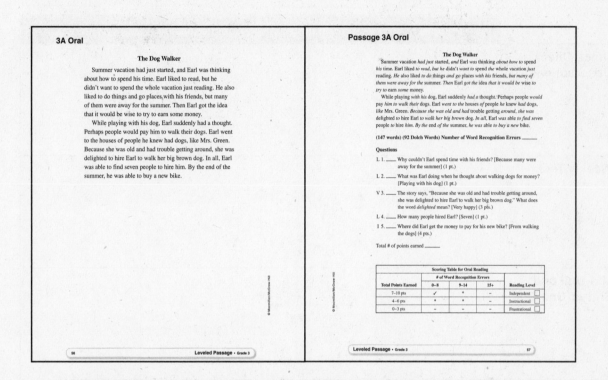

Below Level	Approaching Level	On Level
Grade 1 passage	Grade 2 passage	Grade 3 passage

© Macmillan/McGraw-Hill

Student Record-Keeping Chart

Name _____ Date _____

	Phonics	Vocabulary	Comprehension	Fluency
Quick-Check Observations				
Weekly Test				
Mid-Unit and End-of-Unit Test				
Fluency Assessment				
Leveled Passages				

© Macmillan/McGraw-Hill

Assessment • Assessment Forms

Class Record-Keeping Chart

Student Name	Week 1 Date:	Week 2 Date:	Week 3 Date:	Week 4 Date:	Week 5 Date:

Assessment Schedule

Assessment/Purpose(s)	Time(s)
Quick Phonics Screener	Beginning, middle, and end of year
Letter Naming Fluency (K–2 only)	Beginning, middle, and end of year
Phoneme Segmentation Fluency	Beginning, middle, and end of year
Sight Word Fluency	Beginning, middle, and end of year
Fluency Assessment	Beginning, middle, and end of year
Leveled Text Passages	Beginning, middle, and end of year
Weekly Assessment	At the end of each week
Mid-Unit Assessment	Week 2 of each unit
End-of-Unit Assessment	Week 5 of each unit
Informal Observation (Quick Check)	Daily, ongoing

QPS

Quick Phonics Screener, Standard Version

Jan Hasbrouck, Ph.D.
© 2005 JH Consulting

*The purpose of the Quick Phonics Screener (QPS)
is to provide informal diagnostic information that can be used
to help (a) PLAN a student's instructional program in basic word
reading skills, and (b) MONITOR THE PROGRESS or
IMPROVEMENT in phonics skill development. The QPS has
not been normed or standardized. It is meant to be used as
an informal classroom assessment tool.*

Directions for Administration and Scoring

1. Say to the student:

    "I'm going to ask you to read some letters, words, and sentences to me so I can find out what kinds of words are easy for you to read and what kinds of words you still need to learn. I want you to try to do your best. We probably won't do this whole page; we'll stop if it gets too hard. Do you have any questions?"

    Start the QPS assessment where you believe the student's skills are fairly strong. For beginning readers (K–1st level) start with sounds or letter names.

    For the *NAMES* task, have the student name the letter Q, not the *qu* digraph. For the *SOUNDS* task, have the student give you the short sound for each of the vowels. If the student says the long sound (letter name), say: *"That is one sound that letter makes. Do you know the short sound for that letter?"* For the letter *c* ask for the "hard sound" /k/ as in *cat*. For the letter *g* ask for the "hard sound" /g/ as in *gas*. For the letter *y* ask for the /y/ sound as in *yes*. If the student offers a correct alternate sound for these letters, you should say, *"Yes, that is one sound for that letter. Do you know another sound that letter makes?"*

    Most students in 4th grade and above would not be given the letter names/sounds task. Letter names would usually only be given to K-1st students. (If a student reads 6/10 or more in Task 2a, you may skip Task 1 Letter Sounds).

2. If the student has difficulty (half or fewer correct on any task) move up the page to an easier task. If the student does well (more than half correct on a task), move down to a harder task.

3. On Tasks 2–6: If the student reads all or almost all words correctly on part (a) of the task (reading words), you may want to skip part (b) of the task (reading sentences). If the next task is difficult for the student you can go back and complete the part of a previous task that was skipped.

4. When the student is reading the words in text, only count errors on the target words (those underlined and in italics).

5. Stop the assessment when the student appears frustrated or tired. It is OK to stop in the middle of a task. Not all tasks must be administered, but try to assess as many as possible so you will have sufficient information to plan instruction or monitor progress.

Phonics Assessment

6. Mark errors and make notes/comments to help you remember how the student responded. Note that in Task 9, students read the entire word, not syllable-by-syllable. The teacher's copy is written in syllables to facilitate marking/recording of errors within a word.

7. The QPS is scored by each individual task *only*. Record the ratio of correct responses over the total number possible, (e.g., 13/21 or 8/10 for each task). A chart format can be helpful for reporting QPS results.

1. Letters		Score
(a) Names	N/A not administered	_____ /26
(b) Sounds		18 /21 cons. 4 /5 vowels
2. VC and CVC		Score
(a) List		8 /10
(b) Text		17 /20
3. Consonant Digraphs		Score
(a) List		6 /10
(b) Text		4 /10

8. The grade level listed above each task is an approximate level at which those phonics skills are often taught. **NOTE**: *Results from the QPS **CANNOT** be used to determine a student's grade level performance in reading, only strengths/needs in key phonics and decoding skills.*

Quick Phonics Screener – Standard Version

Task 1(a)	m t a s i r d f o
	g l h u c n b j k
Task 1(b)	y e w p v qu x z

| Task 2(a) | wat   fod   leb   tum   pon |
| | sib   cug   raf   mip   hev |

Task 2(b)	Sam and Ben hid the gum.
	Pat had a nap in bed.
	Mom had a top on a big pot.
	Tim can sit in a tub.

| Task 3(a) | shap   ming   gack   whum   pith |
| | chan   thog   kosh   mich   whaf |

| Task 3(b) | That duck had a wet wing.   Brad hit a log with a whip. |
| | When can Chip pack?   A fish is in that tub. |

| Task 4(a) | clab   trin   snaf   greb   slad |
| | fosp   lonk   mant   jast   sund |

| Task 4(b) | Glen will swim past the raft in the pond. |
| | The frog must flip and spin and jump. |

| Task 5(a) | sice   nole   fune   moze   vate |
| | rine   lade   sile   gane   fote |

| Task 5(b) | Mike and Jane use a rope to ride the mule. |
| | Pete had five tapes at home. |

Phonics Assessment

Quick Phonics Screener - Standard Version

Task 6(a)	cort	pirk	varb	serl	surd
	tarn	forp	murk	tirn	kerm

Task 6(b)	The tar on his torn shirt burned and hurt him.
	The bird hid under the short ferns in the park.

Task 7(a)	litch	mudge	glux	quam	celp
	gerb	knaz	gnap	wrill	ralk

Task 7(b)	The cider is in the wrong cup.
	She ran to the center of the bridge.
	I will stitch a knot on the quilt.
	The giant can gnaw on the box.

Task 8	foat	roast	frea	creak	moom	scoop	raim	waist
	folt	scold	dray	gray	chout	mount	poid	join
	moy	royal	vaul	fault	praw	straw	koe	toe
	frew	jewel	palk	scald	pigh	fight		

Task 9(a)	mascot	basket	moment	bacon	handle
	puzzle	cartoon	order	escape	chowder

Task 9(b)	amputate	liberty	dominate	elastic	entertain
	practical	innocent	electric	volcano	segregate

Task 9(c)	particular	contaminate	community	superior	vitality
	evaporate	inventory	prehistoric	solitary	emergency

Task 10	discount	dismiss	nonsense	nonstop	index	intent
	prefix	prepare	return	regard	unable	uncertain
	confident	concert	station	motion	famous	joyous
	madness	witness	portable	drinkable	fastest	dampest
	mouthful	fearful	honorary	literary	instrument	fragment

Student _____ Teacher _____ Date _____

Grades K-1

1. Letters

(a) Names							Score	(b) Sounds							Score
	m	t	a	s	i	r			/m/	/t/	/a/	/s/	/i/	/r/	
	d	f	o	g	l	h			/d/	/f/	/o/	/g/	/l/	/h/	/21 cons.
	u	c	n	b	j	k			/u/	/k/	/n/	/b/	/j/	/k/	
	y	e	w	p	v	qu			/y/	/e/	/w/	/p/	/v/	/kw/	
	x	z					/27		/ks/	/z/					/5 vowels

Grade 1

2. VC and CVC

					Comments	Score
(a) In List	wat	fod	leb	tum		
	pon	sib	cug	raf		
	mip	hev				/10
(b) In Text	*Sam* and *Ben* *hid* the *gum*. *Pat* *had* a *nap* *in* *bed*.					
	Mom *had* a *top* *on* a *big* *pot*. *Tim* *can* *sit* *in* a *tub*.					/20

Grade 1

3. Consonant Digraphs

					Comments	Score
(a) In List	shap	ming	gack	whum		
	pith	chan	thog	kosh		
	mich	whaf				/10
(b) In Text	*That* *duck* had a wet *wing*. *Brad* hit a log *with* a *whip*.					
	When can *Chip* *pack*? A *fish* is in *that* tub.					/10

Grade 1

4. CVCC and CCVC

					Comments	Score
(a) In List	clab	trin	snaf	greb		
	slad	fosp	lonk	mant		
	jast	sund				/10
(b) In Text	*Glen* will *swim* *past* the *raft* in the *pond*.					
	The *frog* *must* *flip* and *spin* and *jump*.					/10

Grades 1-2

5. Silent E

					Comments	Score
(a) In List	sice	nole	fune	moze		
	vate	rine	lade	sile		
	gane	fote				/10
(b) In Text	*Mike* and *Jane* *use* a *rope* to *ride* the *mule*.					
	Pete had *five* *tapes* at *home*.					/10

Grades 1-2

6. R-Control Vowels

(a) In List				Comments	Score
cort	pirk	varb	serl		
surd	tarn	forp	murk		
tirn	kerm				/10

(b) In Text	Comments	Score
The _tar_ on his _torn_ _shirt_ _burned_ and _hurt_ him.		
The _bird_ hid _under_ the _short_ _ferns_ in the _park_.		/10

Grades 1-3

7. Advanced Consonants (–tch, -dge, -x, qu, soft c & g, kn, gn, wr, -lk)

(a) In List				Comments	Score
litch	mudge	glux	quam		
celp	gerb	knaz	gnap		
wrill	ralk				/10

(b) In Text		Comments	Score
The _cider_ is in the _wrong_ cup.	She ran to the _center_ of the _bridge_.		
I will _stitch_ a _knot_ on the _quilt_.	The _giant_ can _gnaw_ on the _box_.		/10

Grades 1-3

8. Vowel Teams

oa, ea, oo, ai, ol, ay, ou, oi, oy, au, aw, oe, ew, al, igh							Comments	Score
foat	roast	frea	creak	moom	scoop	raim		
waist	folt	scold	dray	gray	chout			
mount	poid	join	moy	royal	vaul	fault		
praw	straw	koe	toe	frew	jewel	palk		
scald	pigh	fight						/30

Grades 2, 3, 4-6+

9. Multi-Syllable

(a) 2-Syllable				Comments	Score
mas-cot	bas-ket	mo-ment	ba-con		
han-dle	puz -zle	car-toon	or-der		
es-cape	chow-der				/10

(b) 3-Syllable				Comments	Score
am-pu-tate	lib-er-ty	dom-in-ate	e-las-tic		
en-ter-tain	prac-ti-cal	in-no-cent	e-lec-tric		
vol-ca-no	seg-re-gate				/10

(c) 4-Syllable				Comments	Score
par-tic-u-lar	con-tam-in-ate	com-mu-ni-ty	su-per-i-or		
vi-tal-i-ty	e-vap-or-ate	in-ven-tor-y	pre-his-tor-ic		
sol-i-tar-y	e-mer-gen-cy				/10

Grades 2, 3, 4-6+

10. Prefixes and Suffixes

dis-, non-, in-, pre-, re-, un-, con-, -tion, -ous, -ness, -able, -est, -ful, -ary, -ment					Comments	Score
discount	dismiss	nonsense	nonstop	index		
intent	prefix	prepare	return	regard		
unable	uncertain	confident	concert	station		
motion	famous	joyous	madness	witness		
portable	drinkable	fastest	dampest	mouthful		
fearful	honorary	literary	instrument	fragment		/30

Phonics Assessment

Introduction

What Is Fluency?

Fluency is the critical bridge between two key elements of reading—decoding and comprehension. In its 2000 report, the National Reading Panel defined it as "the ability to read text quickly, accurately, and with proper expression." Fluency has several dimensions. Successful readers must decode words accurately. But they must move beyond decoding and recognize words in connected text quickly and automatically. They must also read with expression in order to bring meaningful interpretation to the text. All three dimensions—accurate decoding, automaticity, and ability to read expressively—work together to create effective comprehension and overall success in reading.

In its 1994 study of reading, the National Assessment of Educational Progress (NAEP) established a clear connection between fluency and comprehension. NAEP defined fluency as the ease or "naturalness" of reading. It recognized certain key elements as contributing to fluency. These included the reader's grouping or phrasing of words as shown through intonation, stress, and pauses and the reader's adherence to the author's syntax. They also included expressiveness as reflected by the reader's interjection of a sense of feeling, anticipation, or characterization in oral reading. These elements are called *prosody*. When readers use appropriate volume, tone, emphasis, and phrasing, they give evidence of comprehension. They demonstrate that they are actively constructing meaning from the text.

Why Is Fluency Important?

Fluency is critical because it directly impacts the comprehension process. For years, teachers thought that if students could decode words accurately, they would become strong readers. Fluency, which has been referred to as a "neglected" aspect of reading, received little attention. Now it is recognized as one of the five critical components of reading.

Researchers have pointed out that people can successfully focus on only one thing at a time. They can, however, do more than one thing at a time if one of those things is so well learned that it can be done automatically. In its simplest form, reading can be seen as (1) word identification or decoding and (2) comprehension, or the active construction of meaning. Effective readers cannot focus on both of these processes at the same time. If a reader is focused almost entirely on decoding, that reader will have few resources left over for constructing meaning. Only when readers can read the words in connected text automatically are they free to focus their attention on making inferences, drawing conclusions, and applying other critical thinking skills associated with constructing meaning.

A fluent reader generally reads with speed and accuracy, but in addition usually displays these kinds of behaviors:

- Recognizes words automatically
- Applies graphophonic, semantic, and syntactic cues to recognize unfamiliar words
- Segments texts into meaningful chunks
- Emulates the sounds and rhythms of spoken language while reading aloud

A nonfluent reader, in contrast, may display these kinds of behaviors:

- Reads slowly and laboriously
- Processes text word-by-word in a choppy manner
- Frequently ignores punctuation
- Fails to use meaningful phrasing
- Shows little certainty when reading high-frequency words

Fluency does not mean only rapid reading. Occasionally, you will come across a nonfluent reader who is able to read text rapidly but fails to use appropriate phrasing. This reader often ignores meaning and punctuation. As a result, this reader struggles to answer questions about what has been read and fails to grasp the intent of the text.

Why Assess Fluency?

Students need to be fluent in order to be proficient readers. Their oral reading fluency can be improved through explicit training, but you need to assess their fluency level before you can determine what specific fluency-building activities and materials will be appropriate. In addition, students excel in reading when they are given opportunities to read as much connected text as possible at their independent level. Fluency assessment helps you determine what this level is.

The oral reading fluency assessments in this book answer this question: *How many words can a student read aloud per minute and how many of these words are read correctly*? This book also helps you observe reading performance beyond speed and accuracy by providing a rubric similar to the one developed by NAEP. This 4-level rubric on page 28 takes into account additional aspects of fluency, such as prosody.

How and When to Assess

Kindergarten through Early First Grade

Until children can decode and automatically recognize many words by sight, they cannot be expected to read aloud effortlessly and expressively. That is why formally assessing their oral reading fluency at this early stage is not recommended. However, it is highly recommended that kindergarten children be involved in fluency-building activities, such as listening to books being read aloud and imitating auditory models of natural speech. Towards the end of kindergarten, children can be given opportunities to reread familiar, predictable, and decodable text to build fluency.

Some assessments for children at these grade levels are considered valuable. By assessing letter naming, phoneme segmentation, and sight word fluency during kindergarten and the early part of Grade 1, teachers can determine what type of fluency-building activities and materials to provide. Assessments for these skill areas appear on pages 32–37.

Midyear of Grade 1 through Grade 6

Curriculum-based assessment of oral reading fluency is administered by asking a student to do a timed reading of a carefully selected on-level passage. As the student reads, you follow along in a copy of the same text and record errors such as omissions, substitutions, misreadings, insertions of words or parts of words, and hesitations of more than three seconds. Self-corrections and repetitions are not considered errors. To calculate the number of words read correctly in one minute, subtract the number of errors from the total number of words read. This process should be repeated periodically throughout the school year to monitor growth.

The Fluency Passages

The fluency passages serve two purposes. They can be administered three times a year as benchmark tests to determine if students are on track. They can also be used every unit so that you can monitor progress and determine if students are meeting instructional goals.

Oral Fluency Scale

Prosody Rubric

Level 4
- The student: reads in large, meaningful phrases; may occasionally repeat words or short phrases, but the overall structure and syntax of the passage is not affected; reads at an appropriate rate of speed with expressive interpretation.

Level 3
- The student: reads in three- and four-word phrases; reads primarily in phrases that preserve the passage's syntax and structure; attempts to read expressively; generally reads at an appropriate rate of speed.

Level 2
- The student: reads mainly in two-word phrases, with some longer phrases and at times word-by-word; may group words awkwardly and not connect phrases to the larger context of the passage; reads sections of the passage excessively slowly or quickly.

Level 1
- The student: reads word-by-word, with some longer phrases; does not phrase meaningfully or with an appropriate rate of speed; reads the passage excessively slowly.

Fluency Assessment • Introduction

Curriculum-Based Oral Reading Fluency Norms

Use these norms to interpret your students' oral reading fluency abilities and to tailor instruction to their individual needs. Results are based on a one-minute timed sampling of students reading aloud.

Grade	Percentile	Fall WCPM	Winter WCPM	Spring WCPM
1	90	NA	81	111
	75	NA	47	82
	50	NA	23	53
	25	NA	12	28
	10	NA	6	15
	SD	NA	32	39
2	90	106	125	142
	75	79	100	117
	50	51	72	89
	25	25	42	61
	10	11	18	31
	SD	37	41	42
3	90	128	146	162
	75	99	120	137
	50	71	92	107
	25	44	62	78
	10	21	36	48
	SD	40	43	44
4	90	145	166	180
	75	119	139	152
	50	NA	112	123
	25	68	87	98
	10	45	61	72
	SD	40	41	43
5	90	166	182	194
	75	139	156	168
	50	110	127	139
	25	85	99	109
	10	61	74	83
	SD	45	44	45
6	90	177	195	204
	75	153	167	177
	50	127	140	150
	25	98	111	122
	10	68	82	93
	SD	42	45	44
7	90	180	192	202
	75	156	165	177
	50	128	138	150
	25	102	109	123
	10	79	88	98
	SD	40	43	41
8	90	185	193	199
	75	161	173	177
	50	133	146	151
	25	106	115	124
	10	77	84	97
	SD	43	45	41

A student's scores should fall within a range of ten WCPM above or below the score shown.

KEY
WCPM: Words correct per minute
SD: Average standard deviation of scores

SOURCE Hasbrouck, J. & Tindal, G. (2005) norms for oral reading fluency. Eugene, OR: Behavioral Research & Teaching, University of Oregon.

Administering Fluency Assessments and Using the Fluency Record

Directions

Give a student a reading passage he or she has not seen before. Fluency assessments are always done as "cold reads"; that is, they are done with material that is new to the person being tested. Explain that you would like the student to read the passage out loud and then answer two questions about it. Then say: *When you are ready, you may begin.* Start your stopwatch when the student reads the first word.

1. Follow along on your copy of the passage as the student reads. Place a line through each word that is read incorrectly or omitted. Place a check above each word that is read correctly.

2. If the student substitutes or mispronounces a word, put a line through the word and write the word the student said above it.

3. If the student does not correctly say the word within 3 seconds, say the word for the student and circle the word to mark it as incorrect. Self-corrections and repetitions are not marked as errors.

4. At the end of one minute, stop your stopwatch and place a bracket (]) after the last word read by the student. Have the student finish reading the passage.

5. Read the comprehension questions to the student. Have the student answer the comprehension questions orally.

How to Score

Record the information for each student on the fluency record sheet for that passage.

1. Look at the number in the left margin of the passage, on the same line as the bracket. (Note: In hyphenated words, individual words are counted as one word.) Add to this number all the words before the bracket to figure out how many words the student was able to read in one minute.

2. Count each word you circled or put a line through. The total is the number of errors made. Subtract this number from the number of words read in one minute to arrive at the Oral Reading Fluency Rate, or Words Correct Per Minute score.

3. Use this formula to score Oral Reading Accuracy:

$$\frac{\text{Total No. of Words Read} - \text{No. of Errors}}{\text{Total Number of Words Read}} \times 100$$

4. On the Prosody Rubric, circle 1, 2, 3, or 4 depending on your evaluation of the student's performance. A score of 4 is the highest possible score.

5. Write comments about oral reading performance on the sheet, including the student's ability to answer the comprehension questions.

Letter Naming Fluency Assessment

Instructions for Administering Letter Naming Fluency

1. Place the Letter Naming Fluency record sheet in front of the student.

2. Say these specific directions to the student:

Here are some letters. Tell me the names of as many letters as you can. When I say, "Begin" start here (point to the first letter) *and go across the page. Point to each letter and tell me the name of that letter. If you come to a letter that you don't know, I'll tell it to you. Put your finger on the first letter. Ready, begin.*

3. Start your stopwatch. Follow along with the Letter Naming Fluency record sheet. Put a (/) through letters named incorrectly. Place a check above letters named correctly.

4. At the end of 1 minute, place a bracket (]) after the last letter named and say, *Stop.*

Directions for Scoring

1. If the student does not get any correct letter names within the first 10 letters (1 row), discontinue the task and record a score of zero.

2. If the student hesitates for 3 seconds on a letter, score the letter incorrect, and provide the correct letter to the student.

3. If the student provides the letter sound rather than the letter name, say: *Remember to tell me the letter name, not the sound it makes.* If the student continues providing letter sounds, mark each letter as incorrect, and make a note of this behavior at the bottom of the page.

4. Score a point for each correct letter the student names and record the total number of correct letters at the bottom of the sheet.

5. See the **Letter Naming Fluency Growth Table** on page 37 to obtain a letter naming fluency score.

Name _____ Date _____

Letter Naming Fluency	# correct
g a t X r F C j T z	__/10
K l q z b n y s I O	__/10
A e V u Q Y z M j a	__/10
f i W R g U d z S c	__/10
k M g D o J n p m h	__/10
C N E b u a g w V f	__/10
G Y i d e n S T t c	__/10
R F a m Z I w v C n	__/10
f s P o T W E j k Q	__/10
D U g e A b i y B d	__/10
N f p R F q I K p M	__/10
L a W f U c O b x Z	__/10

Total ___/100

Letter Naming Fluency Assessment

Phoneme Segmentation Fluency Assessment

Instructions for Administering Phoneme Segmentation

1. Make a copy of the Phoneme Segmentation Fluency record sheet. Use this sheet to record student's oral responses.

2. Say these directions to the student:

I am going to say a word. Then, you tell me all the sounds you hear in the word. So if I say, "cat" you will say /k/ /a/ /t/. Let's try one. Tell me all the sounds in "hop."

3. If the student gives the correct response, /h/ /o/ /p/, then commend the student.

4. If the student gives an incorrect response, say: *The sounds in "hop" are /h/ /o/ /p/.* Ask the student to repeat the sounds: *Tell me all the sounds in "hop."*

5. Give the student the first word and start your stopwatch. Place a check above each correct sound segment produced. Put a slash (/) through incorrect sounds.

6. The maximum time for each sound segment is 3 seconds. If the student does not provide the next sound segment within 3 seconds, give the student the next word.

7. At the end of 1 minute, stop presenting words and scoring further responses. Add the number of sound segments produced correctly. Record the total number of sound segments produced correctly on the bottom of the scoring sheet.

Directions for Scoring

1. If the student has not given any sound segments correctly in the first five words, discontinue the task and put a score of zero. (0)

2. Place a check above the sound segments in the word that are correctly pronounced by the student. The student receives 1 point for each correct part of the word.

Both of the following examples are correct segmentations of words:

Word	Student Response	Scoring Procedure	Correct Segments
like	"l…i…k"	/l/ /ī/ /k/	3/3
crack	"k..r..a..k"	/k/ /r/ /a/ /k/	4/4

3. Put a slash through segments pronounced incorrectly.

4. See the **Phoneme Segmentation Fluency Growth Table** on page 37 to obtain a phoneme segmentation fluency score.

Record Sheet

Phoneme Segmentation Fluency		# correct
man /m/ /a/ /n/	thing /th/ /i/ /ng/	___ /6
his /h/ /i/ /z/	kiss /k/ /i/ /s/	___ /6
brand /b/ /r/ /a/ /n/ /d/	match /m/ /a/ /ch/	___ /8
smile /s/ /m/ /ī/ /l/	froze /f/ /r/ /ō/ /z/	___ /8
press /p/ /r/ /e/ /s/	cheat /ch/ /ē/ /t/	___ /7
slope /s/ /l/ /ō/ /p/	tide /t/ /ī/ /d/	___ /7
blend /b/ /l/ /e/ /n/ /d/	gate /g/ /ā/ /t/	___ /8
lost /l/ /o/ /s/ /t/	shop /sh/ /o/ /p/	___ /7
jump /j/ /u/ /m/ /p/	drill /d/ /r/ /i/ /l/	___ /8
those /th/ /ō/ /s/	west /w/ /e/ /s/ /t/	___ /7
plug /p/ /l/ /u/ /g/	rush /r/ /u/ /sh/	___ /7
tape /t/ /ā/ /p/	inch /i/ /n/ /ch/	___ /6

Sight Word Fluency Assessment

Instructions for Administering the Assessment

Give student the assessment sheet, and have the child put his or her finger on the first word in the first row. Explain that you would like the child to read as many words as he or she can in one minute. Tell the child to point to each word and say the word. Then say: *When you are ready, you may begin.* Start your stopwatch, timing the student for one minute as he or she reads the words.

1. Follow along as the child reads. Place a check above each word that is said correctly.

2. Place a line through each word that is read incorrectly or omitted.

3. If the child substitutes or mispronounces a word, put a line through the word and write the word the child said above it.

4. If the child does not correctly say a word within 3 seconds, say the word for the child and mark the word as incorrect.

5. Say *Stop* at the end of one minute and place a bracket (]) after the last word read by the child.

Directions for Scoring

1. Count the total number of words read. This includes the words that are read correctly and incorrectly. Record that number on the table at the bottom of the sheet.

2. Count the number of errors for each line of words in the # of errors column. Record the total number of errors in the bottom table.

3. Use this formula to score Oral Reading Accuracy:

$$\frac{\text{Total No. of Words Read} - \text{No. of Errors}}{\text{Total Number of Words Read}} \times 100$$

Sight Word Fluency					# of errors
and	are	do	for	go	(5)
has	have	he	here	is	(5)
like	little	look	me	my	(5)
play	said	see	she	to	(5)
the	this	was	we	what	(5)
where	with	you	jump	not	(5)
up	too	yes	over	run	(5)
come	good	on	that	very	(5)
help	use	now	very	one	(5)
two	they	her	does	who	(5)
some	of	at	live	into	(5)
many	out	want	under	show	(5)

Total number of words read in one minute	
Number of errors	
Accuracy rate (use Oral Reading Accuracy formula)	

Sight Word Fluency Assessment

AIMSweb® Growth Table
Letter Naming Fluency
Multi-year Aggregate

Grade	%ile	Fall		Winter		Spring		ROI
		Num	LNC	Num	LNC	Num	LNC	
K	90		37		55		65	0.8
	75		25		45		54	0.8
	50		11		33		42	0.9
	25	13377	3	12037	20	12653	31	0.8
	10		0		8		19	0.5
	Mean		15		33		42	0.8
	StdDev		15		17		18	
1	90		65		76		79	0.4
	75		55		66		69	0.4
	50		44		55		58	0.4
	25	10887	32	2518	44	1455	47	0.4
	10		22		32		36	0.4
	Mean		44		55		58	0.4
	StdDev		17		17		17	

Num = Number of Students   **LNC** = Letter Names Correct   **ROI** = Rate Of Improvement
ROI is Spring Score minus Fall Score (or Winter minus Fall) divided by 36 weeks (or 18 weeks)

AIMSweb® Growth Table
Phoneme Segmentation Fluency
Multi-year Aggregate

Grade	%ile	Fall		Winter		Spring		ROI
		Num	PC	Num	PC	Num	PC	
K	90		44		48		62	0.5
	75		32		34		51	0.5
	50		14		14		37	0.6
	25	1870	3	13234	5	14103	15	0.3
	10		0		0		5	0.1
	Mean		19		20		35	0.4
	StdDev		17		19		22	
1	90		56		62		67	0.3
	75		46		54		59	0.4
	50		33		43		50	0.5
	25	13615	15	10197	31	8269	39	0.7
	10		6		16		26	0.6
	Mean		31		42		48	0.5
	StdDev		19		18		16	

Num = Number of Students   **PC** = Phonemes Correct   **ROI** = Rate Of Improvement
ROI is Spring Score minus Fall Score (or Winter minus Fall) divided by 36 weeks (or 18 weeks)

Fluency Assessment Norms

Saving Up

My class planned a trip to the aquarium. We decided
to raise money for everyone's admission ticket. We earned
the money by having a Good-to-Eat Sale at school.

Each morning for a week, everyone brought in
something that was both delicious and healthy. I brought
some enormous bran muffins. Miss Hansen brought in
granola bar cookies. Other students brought raisins, carrot
sticks, and banana bread.

We had a wide assortment of treats to sell. We set
up our table where the school buses and cars dropped off
their passengers. Each morning, we arranged the goods on
the table.

As students were dropped off, they saw the delicious
foods. Everyone was surprised to see what was for sale.
No one could pass our table without stopping.

The sale was a huge success. We earned enough
money for everyone to attend the class trip. The class
cannot wait to see all of the sharks and the rare fish
at the aquarium.

1. How did the class earn money for their trip?

2. What did the class mean by foods that were "good to eat"?

© Macmillan/McGraw-Hill

Oral Fluency Record Sheet

Name _____   Date _____

Oral Reading Accuracy: _____%   Circle: Fall   Winter   Spring

Oral Reading Fluency Score: _____ words per minute

Prosody Rubric: (Circle Score) 1 2 3 4

Comprehension Question Responses

#1 _____

#2 _____

Saving Up

	My class planned a trip to the aquarium. We decided
10	to raise money for everyone's admission ticket. We earned
19	the money by having a Good-to-Eat Sale at school.
30	Each morning for a week, everyone brought in
38	something that was both delicious and healthy. I brought
47	some enormous bran muffins. Miss Hansen brought in
55	granola bar cookies. Other students brought raisins, carrot
63	sticks, and banana bread.
67	We had a wide assortment of treats to sell. We set
78	up our table where the school buses and cars dropped off
89	their passengers. Each morning, we arranged the goods on
98	the table.
100	As students were dropped off, they saw the delicious
109	foods. Everyone was surprised to see what was for sale.
119	No one could pass our table without stopping.
127	The sale was a huge success. We earned enough
136	money for everyone to attend the class trip. The class
146	cannot wait to see all of the sharks and the rare fish
158	at the aquarium. 161

Number of words read correctly: _____   Number of errors made: _____

Snakes of Many Colors

You might think snakes do not need protection, but they do. Certain kinds of mammals, such as pigs and mongooses, prey on snakes. Large birds, such as the serpent eagle, think they make fine meals. Even other snakes, such as the King Cobra, will hunt certain snakes.

Snakes often use colors to protect themselves from predators. The bright colors of some snakes, like the Mangrove snake, warn enemies that the snake is poisonous. Other snakes only pretend to be poisonous. The bright red, black, and white scales of the Pueblan milk snake, which are arranged in bands, make animals think the snake is poisonous even though it is not.

Snakes also use their colors to hide themselves from predators. For example, the bright green cat snake lives high in a tree in the rainforest. The snake stays coiled around a branch during the day. It looks just like a vine, fooling animals that might want to make it their dinner.

These snakes need their colorful scales to stay safe. After all, it is a dangerous world, even for a snake.

1. How do snakes use color to protect themselves?
2. Why is the world dangerous for snakes?

Oral Fluency Record Sheet

Name _____ Date _____

Oral Reading Accuracy: _____%   Circle: Fall   Winter   Spring
Oral Reading Fluency Score: _____ words per minute
Prosody Rubric: (Circle Score) 1 2 3 4
Comprehension Question Responses
#1 _____
#2 _____

Snakes of Many Colors

8	You might think snakes do not need protection, but they do. Certain kinds of mammals, such as pigs and
19	
28	mongooses, prey on snakes. Large birds, such as the serpent eagle, think they make fine meals. Even other
37	snakes, such as the King Cobra, will hunt certain snakes.
47	Snakes often use colors to protect themselves from
55	predators. The bright colors of some snakes, like the
64	Mangrove snake, warn enemies that the snake is poisonous.
73	Other snakes only pretend to be poisonous. The bright red,
83	black, and white scales of the Pueblan milk snake, which
93	are arranged in bands, make animals think the snake is
103	poisonous even though it is not.
109	Snakes also use their colors to hide themselves
117	from predators. For example, the bright green cat snake
126	lives high in a tree in the rainforest. The snake stays coiled
138	around a branch during the day. It looks just like a vine,
150	fooling animals that might want to make it their dinner.
160	These snakes need their colorful scales to stay safe.
169	After all, it is a dangerous world, even for a snake. **180**

Number of words read correctly: _____   Number of errors made: _____

© Macmillan/McGraw-Hill

Sun Facts

The sun is important to everything on Earth. Light and heat from the sun give warmth and energy to all life on the planet.

But the sun is really just a star. It looks larger because it is much closer to us than other stars. Compared with other stars, the sun is just medium-sized. But compared with the earth, it is very large indeed. If the sun were a hollow ball, it would take one million Earth-sized balls to fill it up.

The temperature of any place on Earth depends on the position of the sun. Places near the equator are hot because the sun shines almost directly overhead at noon. On the other hand, places near the North Pole and the South Pole are cold. This is because the sun almost never rises above the horizon there.

Scientists know a good deal about the sun, but they still have much to learn. As they learn, they hope to find better ways to use the sun's power on Earth.

1. Why is the sun important to everything on Earth?
2. Which sun fact did you find most interesting? Why?

Oral Fluency Record Sheet

Name _____   Date _____

Oral Reading Accuracy: _____%   Circle: Fall   Winter   Spring
Oral Reading Fluency Score: _____ words per minute
Prosody Rubric: (Circle Score) 1 2 3 4
Comprehension Question Responses
#1 _____
#2 _____

Sun Facts

	The sun is important to everything on Earth. Light
9	and heat from the sun give warmth and energy to all life
21	on the planet.
24	But the sun is really just a star. It looks larger
35	because it is much closer to us than other stars. Compared
46	with other stars, the sun is just medium-sized. But
55	compared with the earth, it is very large indeed. If the sun
67	were a hollow ball, it would take one million Earth-sized
78	balls to fill it up.
84	The temperature of any place on Earth depends on
93	the position of the sun. Places near the equator are hot
104	because the sun shines almost directly overhead at noon.
113	On the other hand, places near the North Pole and the South
125	Pole are cold. This is because the sun almost never rises
136	above the horizon there.
140	Scientists know a good deal about the sun, but they
150	still have much to learn. As they learn, they hope to find
162	better ways to use the sun's power on Earth. 171

Number of words read correctly: _____   Number of errors made: _____

Fruit Fun

Ellen's favorite pastime was making things, so she was delighted when her aunt sent her a box of modeling clay. The clay was soft and gooey, and Ellen could press and mold it into all kinds of shapes. Ellen started by creating different kinds of fruits—apples, bananas, oranges, pears, plums, grapefruit, peaches, and lemons. She arranged her best pieces of fruit in a fancy china bowl, and when her mother saw the bowl, she was amazed at how real the fruit looked. That gave Ellen and her mother an idea, and together they set the pretty bowl in the center of the dining room table.

That evening when Dad came home, he immediately noticed the fruit bowl.

"Those peaches look so ripe and delicious!" Dad exclaimed.

Ellen started laughing and she couldn't stop.

"What are you laughing at?" Dad demanded.

Dad reached out and chose the prettiest peach. Right away he realized why Ellen was laughing.

"You completely fooled me," he said. "This peach certainly looks good enough to eat."

1. What did Ellen make with the modeling clay?
2. Why did Ellen laugh when her father said the peaches look delicious?

© Macmillan/McGraw-Hill

Oral Fluency Record Sheet

Name _____   Date _____

Oral Reading Accuracy: _____%   Circle: Fall   Winter   Spring
Oral Reading Fluency Score: _____ words per minute
Prosody Rubric: (Circle Score) 1 2 3 4
Comprehension Question Responses
#1 _____
#2 _____

Fruit Fun

	Ellen's favorite pastime was making things, so
7	she was delighted when her aunt sent her a box of
18	modeling clay. The clay was soft and gooey, and Ellen
28	could press and mold it into all kinds of shapes.
38	Ellen started by creating different kinds of
45	fruits—apples, bananas, oranges, pears, plums,
51	grapefruit, peaches, and lemons. She arranged her
58	best pieces of fruit in a fancy china bowl, and when
69	her mother saw the bowl, she was amazed at how real
80	the fruit looked. That gave Ellen and her mother an
90	idea, and together they set the pretty bowl in the
100	center of the dining room table.
106	That evening when Dad came home, he
113	immediately noticed the fruit bowl.
118	"Those peaches look so ripe and delicious!"
125	Dad exclaimed.
127	Ellen started laughing and she couldn't stop.
134	"What are you laughing at?" Dad demanded.
141	Dad reached out and chose the prettiest peach.
149	Right away he realized why Ellen was laughing.
157	"You completely fooled me," he said. "This
164	peach certainly looks good enough to eat." 171

© Macmillan/McGraw-Hill

Number of words read correctly: _____   Number of errors made: _____

Chimps That Talk

Have you ever been to the zoo and watched the chimpanzees? Chimpanzees are among the most playful, curious, and interesting animals at the zoo. They often entertain visitors by dancing around, waving their arms, and making hooting noises. Often they come right up to visitors as if they want to have a chat.

For many years, scientists have watched chimpanzees use grunts, hoots, and howls to tell each other about things like food and danger. Scientists wondered if chimpanzees could talk with humans and decided to try to teach them sign language. In sign language, hand and finger movements are used to mean different things.

At first, the chimpanzees would copy the signs the scientists made. For example, the scientist would make the signs for "I want to eat" as the chimpanzees ate a meal and the chimps would copy them. Later, the chimpanzees would make the sign "I want to eat" all by themselves. After a while, chimpanzees learned to make their own signs to show what they wanted.

Would you like to have a conversation with a chimpanzee? Maybe someday you will.

1. What is "Chimps That Talk" mostly about?
2. How do chimpanzees communicate?

Oral Fluency Record Sheet

Name _____ Date _____

Oral Reading Accuracy: _____%   Circle: Fall Winter Spring
Oral Reading Fluency Score: _____ words per minute
Prosody Rubric: (Circle Score) 1 2 3 4
Comprehension Question Responses
#1 _____
#2 _____

Chimps That Talk

	Have you ever been to the zoo and watched the
10	chimpanzees? Chimpanzees are among the most playful,
17	curious, and interesting animals at the zoo. They often
26	entertain visitors by dancing around, waving their arms,
34	and making hooting noises. Often they come right up to
44	visitors as if they want to have a chat.
53	For many years, scientists have watched chimpanzees
60	use grunts, hoots, and howls to tell each other about things like
72	food and danger. Scientists wondered if chimpanzees could
80	talk with humans and decided to try to teach them sign
91	language. In sign language, hand and finger movements are
100	used to mean different things.
105	At first, the chimpanzees would copy the signs the
114	scientists made. For example, the scientist would make the
123	signs for "I want to eat" as the chimpanzees ate a meal and the
137	chimps would copy them. Later, the chimpanzees would make
146	the sign "I want to eat" all by themselves. After a while,
158	chimpanzees learned to make their own signs to show what
168	they wanted.
170	Would you like to have a conversation with a chimpanzee?
180	Maybe someday you will. **184**

Number of words read correctly: _____   Number of errors made: _____

Plants in Danger

Did you know that some plants are endangered? One in eight plants on Earth is dying out, and we may never see them again.

Scientists call a plant endangered if they expect it to die off completely in the next 20 years. They hope that special efforts will be made to protect the plant so that it can continue to survive.

There are several reasons why some plants are endangered. People damage the homes of many kinds of plants when they build new homes or farms. When they cut down trees to clear the land, they destroy the places that have been the plants' homes. In some places, too many sheep or other animals graze on the land and eat all the plants that grew there. Sometimes areas along the coast are filled in for homes and businesses. The plants that grew there are destroyed.

A group called Green Kids has gotten together to teach about endangered plants and to show that kids can make a difference. Each spring, Green Kids visit schools across Canada to perform funny skits about the environment. The skits teach kids how to help save our natural world.

1. What does it mean when a plant is endangered?
2. What are two reasons why plants are endangered?

© Macmillan/McGraw-Hill

Oral Fluency Record Sheet

Name _____   Date _____

Oral Reading Accuracy: _____%   Circle: Fall   Winter   Spring

Oral Reading Fluency Score: _____ words per minute

Prosody Rubric: (Circle Score) 1 2 3 4

Comprehension Question Responses

#1 _____

#2 _____

Plants in Danger

	Did you know that some plants are endangered?
8	One in eight plants on Earth is dying out, and we may
20	never see them again.
24	Scientists call a plant endangered if they expect it
33	to die off completely in the next 20 years. They hope that
45	special efforts will be made to protect the plant so that it
57	can continue to survive.
61	There are several reasons why some plants are
69	endangered. People damage the homes of many kinds
77	of plants when they build new homes or farms. When
87	they cut down trees to clear the land, they destroy the
98	places that have been the plants' homes. In some
107	places, too many sheep or other animals graze on the
117	land and eat all the plants that grew there. Sometimes
127	areas along the coast are filled in for homes and
137	businesses. The plants that grew there are destroyed.
145	A group called Green Kids has gotten together
153	to teach about endangered plants and to show that
162	kids can make a difference. Each spring, Green Kids
171	visit schools across Canada to perform funny skits
179	about the environment. The skits teach kids how to
188	help save our natural world. **193**

Number of words read correctly: _____   Number of errors made: _____

How to Use the Leveled Passages

The Leveled Passages are organized by grade level. In order to administer the Leveled Passages assessment efficiently, you should be familiar with the directions, passages, and questions. To administer the assessment, follow these procedures:

1. Select the first passage for the student to read orally. Have the student start reading the passage 2–3 grades below level. For example, a 4th grade student would begin reading the Grade 1 passage.

2. Begin by saying, "I have some passages for you to read. Read the first one aloud. If you find a hard word, try to read it as best you can and continue reading. It is important to remember what you read so you can answer the questions at the end."

3. While the student reads out loud, code the errors or miscues on the scoring sheet. Do not provide any prompting if a student hesitates over a word. If a student hesitates longer than five seconds, simply tell the word to the student.

4. When the student has completed the passage or story, take it away. The student cannot refer to it while answering the questions.

5. Ask the student the comprehension questions as shown on the teacher recording sheet for the passage. Mark correct answers with a point value on the line provided. The point value is in parentheses at the end of each question. A perfect score is 10 points. The total number of points that a student earns is the comprehension score.

6. After giving the first oral reading passage, determine whether the student has been able to read it at an independent level. If so, continue with the next higher passage. Continue until the student reaches frustration level.

Code for Marking Word Recognition Errors	
Each word recognition error is counted as one error. Never count more than one error on any one word.	
Examples	**Marking Word Recognition Errors**
✓ ✓ ✓ The baby cried	1. Put a check mark over words read correctly.
✓ ✓ My friend (went)	2. Circle omissions.
✓ eats ✓ ✓ He ate the pie	3. Draw a line above words that are read with substitutions. Write the substitution above the line.
✓ T ✓ Why are you	4. Place a T above a word that you need to tell student.
✓ ✓ eating R dinner	5. Place an R next to a word the student repeats.
✓ ✓ ✓ See/S a kind person. She	6. Place the student's initial response and an S above a word that is self corrected. Note: Do not score as an error.
✓ ✓ a (red) apple	7. Use parentheses ( ) to enclose a word that is inserted.

Leveled Passage • Introduction

Procedure for Scoring Leveled Passages

1. Count the total number of scorable errors. Write the total number of errors in the space indicated on the teacher recording sheet. Insertions, substitutions, words told to the student by the teacher, and omissions, are counted as errors at each occurrence. Words that are self-corrected and repeated are not counted as errors.

2. If a student mispronounces a proper name, count it as one error for the entire passage, even if the student mispronounces the same name again.

3. On the teacher recording sheet, a table follows the set of questions. Across the table is a series of numbers to designate the number of word recognition errors. In the column on the left hand side is a series of numbers that show the number of points earned. Locate the number of word recognition errors made by the student and circle the appropriate number. Then locate the number of points earned and draw a circle around that number. Find the point where the two circle items intersect. In that space, you will note the following symbols: the (✓) means the student is reading on an independent level; the (*) means the student is reading on an instructional level; and the (-) means the student is reading at a frustrational level.

	# of Word Recognition Errors			
Total Points Earned	**0–4**	**5–7**	**8+**	**Reading Level**
7–10 pts	✓	*	-	Independent ☐
4–6 pts	*	*	-	Instructional ☐
0–3 pts	-	-	-	Frustrational ☑

Scoring Table for Oral Reading

In the above table, for example, the student has made eight word recognition errors and earned two comprehension points. These two figures intersect in an area marked with a hyphen (-). This means the student is reading on a frustrational level; thus the box to the right of the frustrational level is checked. The student is not ready to handle reading text at this level.

Sam

Ana was so sad.

She was moving out of town.

They could not take her black cat, Sam.

The new house was just too little for pets.

Ana let a good friend take Sam.

Ana liked her new home, but she missed Sam.

One day, Ana went to open the door.

There was Sam!

He had walked for days and days to find Ana.

Ana's mother now said he could stay.

Passage 1A Oral

Sam

Ana *was so* sad. *She was* moving *out of* town. *They could not take her black* cat, Sam. *The new* house *was just too little for* pets. Ana *let a good* friend *take* Sam.

Ana liked *her new* home, *but she* missed Sam. *One* day, Ana *went to open the* door. *There was* Sam! *He had* walked *for* days *and* days *to find* Ana. Ana's mother *now said he could* stay.

(71 words) (44 Dolch Words) Number of Word Recognition Errors _____

Questions

L 1. _____ Where was Ana moving? [Out of town] (1 pt.)

L 2. _____ Who was Sam? [Ana's black cat] (1 pt.)

L 3. _____ Why couldn't Sam go to the new house? [The new house was too little for pets.] (1 pt.)

V 4. _____ What did the story mean when it said that Ana "missed" Sam? [Ana wished he was with her.] (3 pts.)

I 5. _____ What did Sam do that would make you think he loved Ana? [He walked for days and days to find her.] (4 pts.)

Total # of points earned _____

	Scoring Table for Oral Reading			
	# of Word Recognition Errors			
Total Points Earned	**0–4**	**5–7**	**8+**	**Reading Level**
7–10 pts	✓	*	–	Independent ☐
4–6 pts	*	*	–	Instructional ☐
0–3 pts	–	–	–	Frustrational ☐

The Race

One day, Tom saw some boys having a race after school. Tom said, "I would like to be a fast runner like those boys."

Tom began to run every day before and after school. Each day, he was able to run faster than the day before. Soon he could run as fast as the other boys. Tom did not win his first few races, but he would not give up.

The next year, there was a race for all the boys at school. Many of the boys ran fast, but Tom ran faster. The other boys ran hard to catch up with him, but not one could do it. Tom won the race and took home the first prize.

Passage 2A Oral

The Race

One day, Tom *saw some* boys having *a* race *after* school. Tom *said*, "*I would like to be a fast* runner *like those* boys."

Tom began *to run every* day *before and after* school. Each day, *he was* able *to run* faster than *the* day *before. Soon he could run as fast as the* other boys. Tom *did not* win *his first* few races, *but he would not give up.*

The next year, *there was a* race *for all the* boys at school. *Many of the* boys *ran fast, but* Tom *ran* faster. *The* other boys *ran* hard *to* catch *up with him, but not one could do it.* Tom won *the* race *and* took home *the first* prize.

(119 words) (77 Dolch words) Number of Word Recognition Errors _____

Questions

L 1. _____ What did Tom see that made him want to be a fast runner? [Some boys having a race] (1 pt.)

L 2. _____ What did Tom do every day before and after school? [He ran.] (1 pt.)

I 3. _____ What did Tom do that would make you think he sticks with something even if things don't go his way? [He did not win the first few races, but he would not give up.] (4 pts.)

V 4. _____ The story says, "The other boys ran hard to catch up with him, but not one could do it." What does "catch up" mean? [Get closer to, or come up to] (3 pts.)

L 5. _____ Why did Tom take home the first prize? [Because he won the race] (1 pt.)

Total # of points earned _____

	Scoring Table for Oral Reading			
	# of Word Recognition Errors			
Total Points Earned	**0–6**	**7–11**	**12+**	**Reading Level**
7–10 pts	✓	*	–	Independent ☐
4–6 pts	*	*	–	Instructional ☐
0–3 pts	–	–	–	Frustrational ☐

The Dog Walker

Summer vacation had just started, and Earl was thinking about how to spend his time. Earl liked to read, but he didn't want to spend the whole vacation just reading. He also liked to do things and go places with his friends, but many of them were away for the summer. Then Earl got the idea that it would be wise to try to earn some money.

While playing with his dog, Earl suddenly had a thought. Perhaps people would pay him to walk their dogs. Earl went to the houses of people he knew had dogs, like Mrs. Green. Because she was old and had trouble getting around, she was delighted to hire Earl to walk her big brown dog. In all, Earl was able to find seven people to hire him. By the end of the summer, he was able to buy a new bike.

The Dog Walker

Summer vacation *had just* started, *and* Earl *was* thinking *about how to* spend *his* time. Earl liked *to read, but he* didn't *want to* spend *the* whole vacation *just* reading. *He* also liked *to do* things *and go* places *with his* friends, *but many of them were away for the* summer. *Then* Earl *got the* idea *that it would be* wise *to try to* earn *some* money.

While playing *with his* dog, Earl suddenly *had a* thought. Perhaps people *would* pay *him to walk their* dogs. Earl *went to the* houses *of* people *he* knew *had* dogs, *like* Mrs. Green. *Because she was old and had* trouble getting *around, she was* delighted *to* hire Earl *to walk her big brown* dog. *In all*, Earl *was* able *to find seven* people *to* hire *him. By the* end *of the* summer, *he was* able *to buy a new* bike.

(147 words) (92 Dolch Words) Number of Word Recognition Errors _____

Questions

L 1. _____ Why couldn't Earl spend time with his friends? [Because many were away for the summer] (1 pt.)

L 2. _____ What was Earl doing when he thought about walking dogs for money? [Playing with his dog] (1 pt.)

V 3. _____ The story says, "Because she was old and had trouble getting around, she was delighted to hire Earl to walk her big brown dog." What does the word *delighted* mean? [Very happy] (3 pts.)

L 4. _____ How many people hired Earl? [Seven] (1 pt.)

I 5. _____ Where did Earl get the money to pay for his new bike? [From walking the dogs] (4 pts.)

Total # of points earned _____

Scoring Table for Oral Reading				
	# of Word Recognition Errors			
Total Points Earned	**0–8**	**9–14**	**15+**	**Reading Level**
7–10 pts	✓	*	–	Independent ☐
4–6 pts	*	*	–	Instructional ☐
0–3 pts	–	–	–	Frustrational ☐

A Feel for Music

Having a real feel for music, Cora loved to play the piano for friends and family. The problem was that she made mistakes because she never found enough time to sit down and practice.

One day, Mrs. Ruiz, the music teacher, announced that there was going to be a concert, and she wanted Cora to play a piece of music of her choice. Very excited, Cora decided to play "My Favorite Things."

Mrs. Ruiz called all of the children to her house to play their pieces a few days before the concert. To Cora's horror, Matt had decided to play "My Favorite Things" too. Matt played the piece perfectly, but he did not put any feeling into his music. However, all Cora could think was that he would play without any mistakes, while she would make mistakes and look silly.

The next day, Cora told Mrs. Ruiz that she did not want to be in the concert. The teacher said sadly, "You are a very good player because you feel the music, but this means little unless you believe in your talent and give it the time it requires."

Passage 4A Oral

A Feel for Music

Having *a* real feel *for* music, Cora loved *to play the* piano *for* friends *and* family. *The* problem *was that she made* mistakes *because she never* found enough time *to sit down and* practice.

One day, Mrs. Ruiz, *the* music teacher, announced *that there was going to be a* concert, *and she* wanted Cora *to play a* piece *of* music *of her* choice. *Very* excited, Cora decided *to play "My* Favorite Things."

Mrs. Ruiz called *all of the* children *to her* house *to play their* pieces *a* few days *before the* concert. *To* Cora's horror, Matt *had* decided *to play* "My Favorite Things" *too.* Matt played *the* piece perfectly, *but he did not put any* feeling *into his* music. However, *all* Cora *could* think *was that he would play* without any mistakes, while *she would make* mistakes *and look* silly.

The next day, Cora told Mrs. Ruiz *that she did not want to be in the* concert. *The* teacher *said* sadly, *"You are a very good* player *because you* feel *the* music, *but this* means *little* unless *you* believe *in your* talent *and give it the* time *it* requires."

(189 words) (107 Dolch Words) Number of Word Recognition Errors _____

Questions

L 1. ____ Why did Cora make mistakes when she played? [Because she didn't practice enough] (1 pt.)

L 2. ____ What song did Cora choose to play at the concert? ["My Favorite Things"] (1 pt.)

L 3. ____ Where did the children go a few days before the concert to play their pieces? [To Mrs. Ruiz's house] (1 pt.)

V 4. ____ What does the word *horror* mean in this story? [Shock or disappointment] (3 pts.)

I 5. ____ Why did Cora decide not to be in the concert? [Because she was afraid of looking foolish if Matt played the song better than she did] (4 pts.)

Total # of points earned _____

Scoring Table for Oral Reading			
	# of Word Recognition Errors		
Total Points Earned	**0–11**	**12–18**	**19+**	**Reading Level**
7–10 pts	✓	*	–	Independent ☐
4–6 pts	*	*	–	Instructional ☐
0–3 pts	–	–	–	Frustrational ☐

The Wolf and the Dog

A scrawny wolf was almost dead with hunger when he happened to meet a house dog who was passing by. "Cousin," said the dog, "your irregular life will soon be the ruin of you. Why don't you work steadily as I do, and get your food regularly given to you?"

"I would have no objection," said the wolf, "if I could only get a place."

"I will arrange that for you if you come with me to my master and share my work," said the dog.

So the wolf and dog went towards the town together. On the way there, the wolf noticed that the hair on a certain part of the dog's neck was very much worn away, so he asked him how that had come about.

"Oh," said the dog, "that is only the place where the collar is put on at night to keep me chained up. It does irritate the neck a bit, but you'll soon get used to it."

"Goodbye to you," said the wolf, "for it is better to be free and starve than be a fat slave."

Passage 5A Oral

The Wolf and the Dog

A scrawny wolf was almost dead with hunger when he happened to meet a house dog who was passing by. "Cousin," said the dog, "your irregular life will soon be the ruin of you. Why don't you work steadily as I do, and get your food regularly given to you?"

"I would have no objection," said the wolf, "if I could only get a place."

"I will arrange that for you if you come with me to my master and share my work," said the dog.

So the wolf and dog went towards the town together. On the way there the wolf noticed that the hair on a certain part of the dog's neck was very much worn away, so he asked him how that had come about.

"Oh," said the dog, "that is only the place where the collar is put on at night to keep me chained up. It does irritate the neck a bit, but you'll soon get used to it."

"Goodbye to you," said the wolf, "for it is better to be free and starve than be a fat slave."

(184 Words) Number of Word Recognition Errors _____

Questions

L 1. _____ Why was the wolf almost dead? [Lack of food] (1 pt.)

I 2. _____ What did the dog do that would make you think he liked the wolf? [He offered to arrange for the wolf to work for his master.] (4 pts.)

L 3. _____ Why was the hair on the dog's neck worn away? [He had to wear a collar at night.] (1 pt.)

V 4. _____ What does the word *irritate* mean in this story? [Make sore] (3 pts.)

L 5. _____ Why does the wolf say goodbye to the dog? [Because he'd rather starve than be chained up] (1 pt.)

Total # of points earned _____

Scoring Table for Oral Reading			
Total Points Earned	**# of Word Recognition Errors**		**Reading Level**
	0–10	**11–18**	**19+**	
7–10 pts	✓	*	–	Independent ☐
4–6 pts	*	*	–	Instructional ☐
0–3 pts	–	–	–	Frustrational ☐

Androcles and the Lion

A slave named Androcles once escaped from his master and fled to the forest. As he wandered about there, he came upon a lion moaning and groaning in acute pain. At first he turned to flee, but then he saw that the lion's paw was all swollen and bleeding due to the presence of a huge thorn. Androcles pulled out the thorn and bound up the paw, after which the lion licked the man's hand in appreciation and the two became fast friends.

Shortly afterwards both Androcles and the lion were captured, and the slave was sentenced to be thrown to the lion after the latter had not been fed for several days. The emperor and all his court came to see the spectacle, and Androcles was led out into the middle of the arena. Soon the ravenous lion was let loose and rushed roaring toward his victim. But as soon as he approached Androcles, he recognized his friend and licked his hand. The emperor, astounded at this, summoned Androcles to him. After hearing the slave's exceptional story, the emperor freed him and released the lion to his native forest.

Passage 6A Oral

Androcles and the Lion

    A slave named Androcles once escaped from his master and fled to the forest. As he wandered about there, he came upon a lion moaning and groaning in acute pain. At first he turned to flee, but then he saw that the lion's paw was all swollen and bleeding due to the presence of a huge thorn. Androcles pulled out the thorn and bound up the paw, after which the lion licked the man's hand in appreciation and the two became fast friends.

    Shortly afterwards both Androcles and the lion were captured, and the slave was sentenced to be thrown to the lion after the latter had not been fed for several days. The emperor and all his court came to see the spectacle, and Androcles was led out into the middle of the arena. Soon the ravenous lion was let loose and rushed roaring toward his victim. But as soon as he approached Androcles, he recognized his friend and licked his hand. The emperor, astounded at this, summoned Androcles to him. After hearing the slave's exceptional story, the emperor freed him and released the lion to his native forest.

(190 words) Number of Word Recognition Errors _____

Questions

L 1. _____ Why was Androcles in the forest? [He fled there after escaping from his master.] (1 pt.)

I 2. _____ What in the story supports the idea that Androcles is both brave and considerate? [He tends to the wounded lion despite the danger.] (4 pts.)

L 3. _____ What was Androcles's sentence after he was captured? [He was to be thrown to the lion after it had not been fed for several days.] (1 pt.)

L 4. _____ Why didn't the lion attack Androcles? [Because he recognized the friend who had helped him in the forest] (1 pt.)

V 5. _____ What does the word *exceptional* mean in this story? [Extraordinary] (3 pts.)

Total # of points earned _____

	Scoring Table for Oral Reading			
	# of Word Recognition Errors			
Total Points Earned	**0–11**	**12–19**	**20+**	**Reading Level**
7–10 pts	✓	*	–	Independent ☐
4–6 pts	*	*	–	Instructional ☐
0–3 pts	–	–	–	Frustrational ☐

At Frog Pond

Jim and Sam were in the woods. They came to a path called "Frog Pond."

"Let's go," said Jim. "We will see lots of frogs."

"How far away is the pond?" asked Sam. "I don't want to get lost."

"Quit acting like a baby," said Jim. "It can't be far."

The boys went on. Soon they came to Frog Pond.

"Look!" said Jim. "There are six frogs on that log."

"Where?" said Sam.

"Come here," said Jim.

Just then a frog jumped onto Sam's head.

"There is a frog on your head," said Jim.

"Quit acting silly," said Sam.

Then a frog jumped onto Jim's head.

"You have a frog on your head," said Sam.

"Quit acting silly," said Jim.

"Let's go home now," said Sam.

On the way, they ran into their pal Bill.

"Your new frog hats look good," said Bill.

Sam and Jim both said, "Quit acting silly."

Bill smiled and went on his way.

Name _____

Directions: Fill in the circle next to the best answer.

1. **What does *quit* mean in the sentence below?**

   > "Quit acting like a baby," said Jim.

   Ⓐ keep still

   Ⓑ stop

   Ⓒ set free

   Ⓓ leave a job

2. **When Sam and Jim *ran into* Bill, they _____.**

   Ⓐ hit him

   Ⓑ met him

   Ⓒ gave him a frog hat

   Ⓓ took him to Frog Pond

3. **Frog Pond had lots of frogs that _____.**

   Ⓐ jumping.

   Ⓑ jumpy.

   Ⓒ jumpily.

   Ⓓ jumped.

4. **This story mostly takes place _____.**

   Ⓐ in the woods

   Ⓑ on the log

   Ⓒ in the pond

   Ⓓ at Sam and Jim's house

5. **This story is funny because _____.**

   Ⓐ everyone acted silly

   Ⓑ frogs were on Jim's and Sam's heads

   Ⓒ Bill liked the frogs

   Ⓓ the frogs jumped off the boys' heads

6. **At the end of the story, Jim and Sam were _____ to Bill.**

   Ⓐ acting

   Ⓑ talked

   Ⓒ talking

   Ⓓ acts

7. **The word ____rhymes with *Sam*.**

   Ⓐ Jim

   Ⓑ far

   Ⓒ hit

   Ⓓ jam

8. **Which word rhymes with <u>six</u>?**

   Ⓐ fix

   Ⓑ sit

   Ⓒ fin

   Ⓓ pig

Grade 3 • Unit 1 • Week 1

Student Evaluation Chart

TESTED SKILLS	Number Correct	Percent Correct
Vocabulary	/3	%
Context clues: sentence clues, 1, 2		
Endings –ing, –s, –ed, 3		
Reading Comprehension	/2	%
Setting, 4		
Plot (ending), 5		
Structural Analysis	/1	%
Endings –s, –ed, –ing, 6		
Phonics	/2	%
Short a, i, 7, 8		
Total Weekly Test Score	/8	%

ANSWER KEY
1. B; 2. B; 3. D; 4. A; 5. B; 6. C; 7. D; 8. A

Jan Sends a Letter

Jan was home with a cold. What could she do?
She wrote a letter.

Tuesday, November 1

Dear Grandpa,

    I hope you are well. Mom and I are planning to visit you this winter. It will be cold here, but hot where you are.

    Can we take a trip to the beach? The beaches where you live are fun. We can go swimming every day. Digging in the sand will be fun too.

    All the classes in our school are selling apples to make money for a trip to a farm in the spring. Some of the money will pay for the buses. We need ten of them.

    Tonight we are going to cut up our pumpkin. We will make a pie with it.

    I have to quit writing now. Write back soon.

                   Love Jan

Jan stepped outside, walked to the mailbox, and slipped the letter in the slot.

"I know Grandpa will write soon," she said.

Name _____

Directions: Fill in the circle next to the best answer.

1. Jan is ____ to visit grandpa in the winter.
   Ⓐ taking
   Ⓑ planning
   Ⓒ hopping
   Ⓓ tipping

2. If you ____ a farm, you might see cows.
   Ⓐ plan
   Ⓑ write
   Ⓒ visit
   Ⓓ trek

3. What does *letter* mean in the sentence below?

   > She wrote a <u>letter</u>.

   Ⓐ mail in envelopes
   Ⓑ symbols of the alphabet
   Ⓒ writings, such as books
   Ⓓ awards

4. Jan wants to go _____ during her visit.
   Ⓐ swiming
   Ⓑ singing
   Ⓒ swimming
   Ⓓ cutting

5. Jan _____ to go to the beach.

   Ⓐ wants

   Ⓑ visits

   Ⓒ sells

   Ⓓ writes

6. **What is true about Jan?**

   Ⓐ She does not like to write.

   Ⓑ She likes to go fishing.

   Ⓒ She loves her grandpa.

   Ⓓ She lives where it is warm in winter.

7. **What time of the year does Jan write to grandpa?**

   Ⓐ spring

   Ⓑ summer

   Ⓒ fall

   Ⓓ winter

Name _____

8. **What sentence is most likely true about Jan?**

   Ⓐ She was very upset that she had a bad cold.

   Ⓑ She didn't think about her cold while writing.

   Ⓒ She does not like cooking with her mom.

   Ⓓ She doesn't like where she lives.

9. **What does Jan do after she writes the letter?**

   Ⓐ She cuts her pumpkin.

   Ⓑ She digs in the sand.

   Ⓒ She walks to the mailbox.

   Ⓓ She buys an apple.

10. **Jan is _____ up a pumpkin.**

   Ⓐ cuting

   Ⓑ cutting

   Ⓒ cuteing

   Ⓓ cutteing

11. **Which word is spelled correctly?**

Ⓐ classes

Ⓑ classs

Ⓒ clases

Ⓓ clasess

12. **What is the class selling to make money for a trip?**

Ⓐ gum

Ⓑ apples

Ⓒ socks

Ⓓ pumpkins

13. **Maybe Jan will pick up _____ at the beach.**

Ⓐ shalls

Ⓑ shells

Ⓒ shills

Ⓓ shulls

Name _____

Student Evaluation Chart

TESTED SKILLS	Number Correct	Percent Correct
Vocabulary	/5	%
Context clues: surrounding words, 1, 2, 3, 4, 5		
Reading Comprehension	/4	%
Setting, 7		
Plot (ending), 9		
Character, 6, 8		
Structural Analysis	/2	%
Plural with es, 11		
Double consonants, 10		
Phonics	/2	%
Short e, o, and u, 12, 13		
Total Weekly Test Score	/13	%

ANSWER KEY
1. B; 2. C; 3. A; 4. C; 5. A; 6. C; 7. C; 8. B; 9. C; 10. B; 11. A; 12. B; 13. B

The Ant in the West

There are many kinds of ants. One kind is the red ant that lives in the West. Before the queen ant lays eggs, her wings drop off. Then she digs a hole and lays eggs. The worker ants help care for the young ants. They find food for them.

These ants don't stop working. They build nests under the ground. If you walk near the ants' nest you will spot it. The ants take away plants around the nest. They put rocks around the nest hole. You may think their work is slow, but they get the job done.

These ants can bite. An ant's sting can hurt. But they do not bite often. In fact, these ants are sold for ant farms. They are not bad pests.

The horned lizard eats these ants. If the ants die out so will the lizards. And that would be sad. If people are smart, they will try to keep them safe.

Name _____

Directions: Fill in the circle next to the best answer.

1. **What does *pests* mean in the sentence below?**

    > Those <u>pests</u> have six legs and 2 sets of wings.

    Ⓐ dogs

    Ⓑ papers

    Ⓒ children

    Ⓓ ants

2. **The _____ eats lots of ants.**

    Ⓐ rocks

    Ⓑ queen

    Ⓒ horned lizard

    Ⓓ people

3. **Who finds food for young ants?**

    Ⓐ the queen

    Ⓑ worker ants

    Ⓒ the young ants

    Ⓓ the horned lizard

4. **This selection is mainly about _____ .**

    Ⓐ what horned lizards eat

    Ⓑ how queen ants lay eggs

    Ⓒ how red ants get food

    Ⓓ how red ants live in the West

Name _____

5. **Which is a detail in the selection?**

    Ⓐ Ants have lots of nests.

    Ⓑ Red ants are sold for ant farms.

    Ⓒ People don't like ants.

    Ⓓ All lizards have horns.

6. **The _____ wings fall off.**

    Ⓐ queen ants'

    Ⓑ queen ant's

    Ⓒ queen ants

    Ⓓ queen antes

7. **Which word is spelled incorrectly?**

    Ⓐ drip

    Ⓑ flag

    Ⓒ step

    Ⓓ slom

8. **Which word is spelled correctly?**

    Ⓐ slim

    Ⓑ stum

    Ⓒ stim

    Ⓓ stam

Grade 3 • Unit 1 • Week 3

Student Evaluation Chart

TESTED SKILLS	Number Correct	Percent Correct
Vocabulary	/3	%
Context clues: unfamiliar words, 1, 2, 3		
Reading Comprehension	/2	%
Main idea, 4		
Details, 5		
Structural Analysis	/1	%
Possessives, 6		
Phonics	/2	%
Blends, 7, 8		
Total Weekly Test Score	/8	%

ANSWER KEY
1. D; 2. C; 3. B; 4. D; 5. B; 6. B; 7. D; 8. A

Whales on the Move

Have you ever gone whale watching? If you go, you may see humpback whales. They may swim up to the boat. They may jump out of the water and slap their flippers. They blow water out of their blowholes.

Every year the whales swim from cold waters to warm waters. They eat seafood such as fish and krill in cold waters. They mate in warm waters.

Only the male humpback whales sing. They face their heads down in the water. They put out their flippers and sing. Clicks! Blips! Trills! People think they sing when they want a mate.

Humpback whales' lungs are the size of a car. That's why they can stay down in the water for a long time.

At low tide a whale can get stuck in low waters. That's bad news. People work hard to get them back into the sea. That's good news.

Name _____

Directions: Fill in the circle next to the best answer.

1. **What does *waters* mean in the sentence below?**

   Dad <u>waters</u> the trees when the sun goes down.

   Ⓐ lots of rain
   Ⓑ wets the ground
   Ⓒ the sea
   Ⓓ makes less strong

2. **The whale fills up its _____ with air.**

   Ⓐ flippers
   Ⓑ krill
   Ⓒ lungs
   Ⓓ waters

3. **When sea water is low, we call this low ____ .**

   Ⓐ tide
   Ⓑ ride
   Ⓒ tidy
   Ⓓ waters

4. **A good title for this selection might be _____ .**

   Ⓐ High Tide
   Ⓑ All Kinds of Krill
   Ⓒ Facts about Whales
   Ⓓ Beached Whales

5. **Which of the following details is NOT in the selection?**

   Ⓐ Whales eat fish.

   Ⓑ Whales mate in warm water.

   Ⓒ Whales have bumps on their bodies.

   Ⓓ Male humpbacks sing.

6. **People think whales sing when they want a _____ .**

   Ⓐ meet

   Ⓑ meat

   Ⓒ mat

   Ⓓ mate

7. **Which of the following is NOT a compound word?**

   Ⓐ humpback

   Ⓑ watching

   Ⓒ blowhole

   Ⓓ seafood

8. **The opposite of *good* is _____ .**

   Ⓐ bade

   Ⓑ bed

   Ⓒ bad

   Ⓓ bede

Name _____

Grade 3 • Unit 1 • Week 4

Student Evaluation Chart

TESTED SKILLS	Number Correct	Percent Correct
Vocabulary	/3	%
Context Clues, 2, 3		
Strategy-homographs, 1		
Reading Comprehension	/2	%
Main Idea, 4		
Details, 5		
Structural Analysis	/1	%
Compound, 7		
Phonics	/2	%
Short a, long a, 6, 8		
Total Weekly Test Score	/8	%

ANSWER KEY
1. B; 2. C; 3. A; 4. C; 5. C; 6. D; 7. B; 8.C

You Think You Have Problems!

I was safe my first nine weeks with Mom. Then some people came and took me away from her. I was scared. I could not stop sobbing.

I kept hearing, "Come Spot, here Spot." I decided they were talking to me. They gave me a warm bed and some toys.

Oh, how I missed my mother! A boy came and petted me. He said, "We love you. You will be fine soon. Sleep, little pup." Then he sat next to my bed. I felt a bit better.

The next day the boy said, "We have to visit the vet. My mom will drive us. The vet will look at your lungs." What is a vet? I was scared. I must plan a way to find my mom.

At the vet's office I saw a cat coming at me. It gazed at me. It hissed at me. I barked. The boy held me and yelled at the cat, "Quit hissing at my pup, you pest!"

He is a smart boy. I like him. He will keep me safe.

Name _____

Directions: Fill in the circle next to the best answer.

1. **What does *gazed* mean in the sentence below?**

    The boy <u>gazed</u> at the picture on the wall.

    Ⓐ made fun of

    Ⓑ took down

    Ⓒ looked for a long time

    Ⓓ looked very upset

2. **What does *missed* mean in the sentence below?**

    We <u>missed</u> the school bus.

    Ⓐ We feel sad.

    Ⓑ We did not hit the mark.

    Ⓒ The bus left without us.

    Ⓓ We did not paint it.

3. **If a cat *hissed*, it most likely would have been _____ .**

    Ⓐ warm

    Ⓑ happy

    Ⓒ cold

    Ⓓ scared

4. **What does *next to* mean in the sentence below?**

    He sat <u>next to</u> my bed.

    Ⓐ close by

    Ⓑ almost as good

    Ⓒ the one coming up

    Ⓓ after this time

5. Spot could not stop sobbing because he was _____ .

Ⓐ happy

Ⓑ wanted to play

Ⓒ sad

Ⓓ safe

6. The main character in this story is _____ .

Ⓐ the boy

Ⓑ the vet

Ⓒ Mom

Ⓓ Spot

7. Which sentence best tells what Spot's problem is?

Ⓐ He wanted to run away.

Ⓑ He didn't like the boy.

Ⓒ He wanted new toys.

Ⓓ He missed his mother.

8. At the end of the story, Spot _____ .

Ⓐ still wanted his mother

Ⓑ still planned to run away

Ⓒ was starting to feel safe

Ⓓ didn't like the vet

Name _____

9. **Most of this story takes place at _____ .**

    Ⓐ the pup's mother's home

    Ⓑ the boy's home

    Ⓒ Spot's bed

    Ⓓ the park

10. **Which word is spelled correctly?**

    Ⓐ caming

    Ⓑ comming

    Ⓒ comeing

    Ⓓ coming

11. **At the end of the story, Spot _____ the boy.**

 (A) life

 (B) locked

 (C) liked

 (D) licked

12. **Spot was a _____ pup.**

 (A) lattle

 (B) little

 (C) lietle

 (D) litel

13. **The cat was _____ at the pup.**

 (A) gazzing

 (B) gazing

 (C) gazzeing

 (D) gazeing

Grade 3 • Unit 1 • Week 5

Student Evaluation Chart

TESTED SKILLS	Number Correct	Percent Correct
Vocabulary	/5	%
Context Clues, 1, 2, 3, 5		
Multiple meaning words, 4		
Reading Comprehension	/4	%
Character, setting, plot, 6, 9		
Problem and solution, 7, 8		
Structural Analysis	/2	%
Drop e before adding -ing, 10, 13		
Phonics	/2	%
Short i, long i, 11, 12		
Total Weekly Test Score	/13	%

ANSWER KEY
1. C; 2. C; 3. D; 4. A; 5. C; 6. D; 7. D; 8. C; 9. B; 10. D; 11. C; 12. B; 13. B

The Bug

I take a tap dancing class with my friend, Jane. We have fun. Each year my class puts on a big show. This year I get to be in it! There are many animal roles. I'm going to be a bug. We will be on a big stage.

Our teacher says that all dancers practice a lot. I practice at home. But sometimes I get tired of doing the same steps. So I try to be a real bug. How does a bug dance? Is it fast or is it slow? I think it is both. I take it slow at first. Then I go fast. Jane taps with me. We are bugs!

It's the day of the big show. I go on stage. What a huge crowd! And they look so close to me! Can I do it? Yes! All that practice has helped. I am a bug. I sing a happy tune and my feet tap and tap and tap.

Name _____

Directions: Fill in the circle next to the best answer.

1. **What does *close* mean in the sentence below?**

And they all look so <u>close</u> to me!

   Ⓐ big

   Ⓑ far

   Ⓒ small

   Ⓓ near

2. **Which word means the opposite of *fast*?**

   Ⓐ go

   Ⓑ stop

   Ⓒ slow

   Ⓓ far

3. **She jumped <u>up</u> into the air and then she came _____.**

   Ⓐ small

   Ⓑ stop

   Ⓒ up

   Ⓓ down

4. **What does the girl do to help her practice her steps?**

   Ⓐ She pretends to be a bug.

   Ⓑ She goes to school.

   Ⓒ She waits backstage.

   Ⓓ She visits a garden.

Name _____

5. What is the story mostly about?

Ⓐ a dancing bug

Ⓑ a girl practicing a dance for a show

Ⓒ a girl turning into a bug

Ⓓ a girl going to school

6. We went _____ after the show.

Ⓐ home

Ⓑ hom

Ⓒ hum

Ⓓ ham

7. Which word is spelled correctly?

Ⓐ danceer

Ⓑ dancer

Ⓒ dancerr

Ⓓ dancr

8. I like the _____ to that song!

Ⓐ tun

Ⓑ tale

Ⓒ ten

Ⓓ tune

Grade 3 • Unit 2 • Week 1

Student Evaluation Chart

TESTED SKILLS	Number Correct	Percent Correct
Vocabulary	/3	%
Context clues: sentence clues, 1		
Antonyms, 2, 3		
Reading Comprehension	/2	%
Summarize, 4, 5		
Structural Analysis	/1	%
Suffix, -er, 7		
Phonics	/2	%
Short o, Long o (o_e), 6 *Short u, Long u* (u_e), 8		
Total Weekly Test Score	/8	%

ANSWER KEY
1. D; 2. C; 3. D; 4. A; 5. B; 6. A; 7. B; 8. D

Tea for Two

It was just after sunset. A huge moon was out. Light gleamed through the trees. Two ants sat on a green leaf. They sat there all day. But now they had to leave. It was time to go home. One ant was ready to leave. The other was not. "I do not want to leave," said the first ant. "I like this leaf."

The other ant said, "No, we must leave. The sun has set. We must go home."

"What will we do at home?" said the first ant.

"We can have tea," said the other ant.

"Tea? We usually have tea in the morning," said the first ant.

"Tea at night is better," said the other ant. "Trust me. We will have tea after sunset. And we can practice for the morning!"

So the two ants left and went home. They had tea at night. And in the morning too!

© Macmillan/McGraw-Hill

Name _____

Directions: Fill in the circle next to the best answer.

1. **What does *usually* mean in the sentence below?**

   > We <u>usually</u> have tea in the morning.

   Ⓐ often
   Ⓑ never
   Ⓒ at night
   Ⓓ every day

2. **One ant asked the other to _____ him.**

   Ⓐ treat
   Ⓑ sunset
   Ⓒ trump
   Ⓓ trust

3. **Which meaning of *gleam* is correct in the sentence below?**

   > The light from the moon will often <u>gleam</u> at night.

   Ⓐ a flash of light
   Ⓑ shine
   Ⓒ set
   Ⓓ darken

4. **Which word means the opposite of *up*?**

   Ⓐ in

   Ⓑ out

   Ⓒ down

   Ⓓ right

5. **First, the ant looked right and then he looked _____.**

   Ⓐ left

   Ⓑ into

   Ⓒ through

   Ⓓ together

6. **Which of the following tells you that the story is a fantasy?**

   Ⓐ it is after sunset

   Ⓑ the moon is out

   Ⓒ the ants can talk

   Ⓓ the ants are sitting on a leaf

7. **Which detail in the story could really happen?**

   Ⓐ ants talking

   Ⓑ ants drinking tea only in the morning

   Ⓒ ants sitting on a leaf

   Ⓓ ants drinking tea at night and in the morning

© Macmillan/McGraw-Hill

8. **What is the story mostly about?**

   Ⓐ one ant trying to get his friend to go home

   Ⓑ ants drinking tea

   Ⓒ the moon shining on a green leaf

   Ⓓ a sun setting and the moon rising

9. **Why did one ant suggest that they drink tea at home?**

   Ⓐ so that they could stay on the leaf a bit longer

   Ⓑ because it was morning

   Ⓒ because the moon was out

   Ⓓ so that his friend would want to go home

10. **The ants sat on a _____ leaf.**

   Ⓐ grean

   Ⓑ grene

   Ⓒ gren

   Ⓓ green

11. **The ants went home to drink _____ .**

   Ⓐ te

   Ⓑ tea

   Ⓒ tee

   Ⓓ teea

12. **One ant wanted the other ant to go _____ with him.**

   Ⓐ hume

   Ⓑ home

   Ⓒ hom

   Ⓓ homm

13. **The moon was _____ and shone through the trees.**

   Ⓐ huge

   Ⓑ hug

   Ⓒ hugg

   Ⓓ hoog

Name _____

Student Evaluation Chart

TESTED SKILLS	Number Correct	Percent Correct
Vocabulary	/5	%
Context clues, 1, 2		
Dictionary: Multiple-meaning words, 3		
Antonyms, 4, 5		
Reading Comprehension	/4	%
Summarize, 8, 9		
Fantasy and reality, 6, 7		
Phonics	/4	%
Long / ē / ee, ea ey, y, 10, 11		
Short /o/o, Long /ō/ē, 12 *Short /u/u, Long /ū/ē, 13*		
Total Weekly Test Score	/13	%

ANSWER KEY
1. A; 2. D; 3. B; 4. C; 5. A; 6. C; 7. C; 8. A; 9. D; 10.D; 11.B; 12.B; 13.A

What Is Your Hobby?

Do you have a hobby? Lots of kids have hobbies. Some like trains. Others like stamps. Some get up early and watch birds fly in the sky. There are so many different hobbies to have. At night you might study the stars. There are many beautiful sights in the sky!

A hobby is easy to have. Just think of something fun. Then do it! Do you like to bake? Baking can be a hobby. You can make pies. Then you can eat them.

Did you ever fly a kite? That is fun, too! You can make kites or buy them. It is easy to fly a kite. You just need a windy day and lots of string.

Or, maybe you like to paint? Art can be a hobby. Just pick up a pencil and begin. There are so many different hobbies out there. Which one will you choose?

Name _____

Directions: Fill in the circle next to the best answer.

1. **What does *sights* mean in the sentence below?**

   There are many beautiful <u>sights</u> in the sky!

   Ⓐ things to do

   Ⓑ things to see

   Ⓒ clouds

   Ⓓ birds

2. **There are many _____ to choose from.**

   Ⓐ hobbys

   Ⓑ hobbyes

   Ⓒ hobbies

   Ⓓ hobbis

3. **This boy _____ kites.**

   Ⓐ flyes

   Ⓑ flys

   Ⓒ flis

   Ⓓ flies

4. **Which of the following sentences is a fact from the story?**

   Ⓐ Hobbies are fun.

   Ⓑ The sky is beautiful at night.

   Ⓒ Flying kites is a hobby.

   Ⓓ Flying kites is fun.

5. How do you know that the sentence below is an opinion?

> Watching birds is fun.

Ⓐ Watching birds is not fun.

Ⓑ It cannot be proven.

Ⓒ People do not watch birds in the morning.

Ⓓ It is not about hobbies.

6. The boy watched the stars at _____ .

Ⓐ nitght

Ⓑ nigt

Ⓒ nite

Ⓓ night

7. Can you _____ your shoes?

Ⓐ tye

Ⓑ ty

Ⓒ tie

Ⓓ ti

8. Which word is spelled correctly?

Ⓐ skies

Ⓑ skys

Ⓒ skyes

Ⓓ skyies

Name _____

Student Evaluation Chart

TESTED SKILLS	Number Correct	Percent Correct
Vocabulary	/3	%
Context clues, 1		
Word Parts: Plural Endings -s and -es, 2, 3		
Reading Comprehension	/2	%
Fact and Opinion, 4, 5		
Phonics	/2	%
Long /ī/i, igh, ie, y, 6, 7		
Structural Analysis	/1	%
Inflectional Ending Change -y to i before adding -es, -ed, 8		
Total Weekly Test Score	/8	%

ANSWER KEY
1. B; 2. C; 3. D; 4. C; 5. B; 6. D; 7. C; 8. A

How Animals Stay Safe

There are different ways animals stay safe. Many fish can tell when danger is near. They make swift motions with their fins. That warns other fish to hide. Some fish live in coral reefs. They have bright scales. This helps them blend in with the bright reefs. Larger fish can't see them.

Other animals also blend in to keep safe. Some bugs can look like twigs. A bird might fly right by the bug to get a drink. The bird wouldn't know there was a bug on the twig. Birds keep safe too. Some birds have eggs with spots. The spots blend in with the nests. Other animals only come out at night. They sleep during the day in hidden places.

Animals try to hide from danger. Only sometimes they can't. Larger animals find them. Even people find them. But animals never stop trying to stay safe. They build homes under the ground. They blend in. They warn others. They protect themselves.

Name _____

Directions: Fill in the circle next to the best answer.

1. **What does *swift* mean in the sentence below?**

   They make <u>swift</u> motions with their fins.

   Ⓐ fast
   Ⓑ on time
   Ⓒ slow
   Ⓓ bright

2. **What is the correct definition of *scales* in the sentence below?**

   Some fish have bright <u>scales.</u>

   Ⓐ objects used to weigh things
   Ⓑ outer skin of some animals
   Ⓒ music notes
   Ⓓ marks used to measure distance

3. **Most animals know when _____ is near.**

   Ⓐ dangur
   Ⓑ danjer
   Ⓒ danger
   Ⓓ dangr

4. **What is the story mostly about?**

   Ⓐ why fish have scales
   Ⓑ how birds eat bugs
   Ⓒ how animals protect themselves
   Ⓓ how fish are brightly colored

Name _____

5. **Why do animals try to blend in?**
- Ⓐ so that other animals can't see them
- Ⓑ so that people will find them
- Ⓒ so that birds will eat them
- Ⓓ so that birds will have spotted eggs

6. **Sometimes a bird will fly by a hidden bug to get a _____ .**
- Ⓐ drink
- Ⓑ drnk
- Ⓒ dink
- Ⓓ drik

7. **The spots help the eggs _____ in with the nest.**
- Ⓐ blened
- Ⓑ blnd
- Ⓒ bled
- Ⓓ blend

8. **The bird _____ see the bug.**
- Ⓐ could'nt
- Ⓑ couldnt
- Ⓒ couldn't
- Ⓓ cudn't

Name _____

Grade 3 • Unit 2 • Week 4

Student Evaluation Chart

TESTED SKILLS	Number Correct	Percent Correct
Vocabulary	/3	%
Context clues: definitions, 1, 2, 3		
Reading Comprehension	/2	%
Summarize, 4, 5		
Phonics	/2	%
Initial and final blends, 6, 7		
Structural Analysis	/1	%
Contractions with "not", 8		
Total Weekly Test Score	/8	%

ANSWER KEY
1. A; 2. B; 3. C; 4. C; 5. A; 6. A; 7. D; 8. C

© Macmillan/McGraw-Hill

The Mail

Do you ever get mail? How does it get to you? Mail can come by train. It can come by truck. It can come by a plane. There are many ways mail can get to your home. But mail did not always come this way.

Before trains were invented, men usually rode on horses. They carried the mail in bags. They rode over different routes. Sometimes there was danger on the road. But these swift riders did not let anything stop them. They rode through the rain and snow. They rode through the night.

After trains were invented, mail was carried that way. Today, huge trucks and planes usually bring the mail. Then it comes to the post office. Skilled workers sort the mail. They review the addresses. They look up zip codes. They send the mail to the right place. This is how the mail comes to your mailbox.

Name _____

Directions: Fill in the circle next to the best answer.

1. **What does *routes* mean in the sentence below?**

   | They rode over different <u>routes.</u> |

   Ⓐ trains

   Ⓑ horses

   Ⓒ letters

   Ⓓ paths

2. **How was the mail usually brought to homes before trains were invented?**

   Ⓐ by car

   Ⓑ by plane

   Ⓒ by horses

   Ⓓ by zip code

3. **The mailman _____ the mail in bags.**

   Ⓐ carrys

   Ⓑ carries

   Ⓒ carryes

   Ⓓ carris

Name _____

4. **What does *usually* mean in the sentence below?**

> Today, huge trucks and planes <u>usually</u> bring the mail.

Ⓐ often

Ⓑ never

Ⓒ sometimes

Ⓓ weekly

5. **Which word means the opposite of *go*?**

Ⓐ left

Ⓑ up

Ⓒ stop

Ⓓ right

6. **What was the author's purpose for writing this story?**

Ⓐ to inform: to tell how mail was delivered long ago and today

Ⓑ to entertain: to tell why we get mail

Ⓒ to inform: to tell how men rode horses long ago

Ⓓ to persuade: to tell how mail is best delivered by horses

7. **Why did the author mention that men on horses used to deliver the mail?**

Ⓐ to explain why people rode horses

Ⓑ to explain how mail was delivered long ago

Ⓒ to show how mail is delivered today

Ⓓ to show how mail was delivered by huge trucks

Name _____

8. **Which of the following is an opinion?**

   Ⓐ Today the mail comes by airplanes.

   Ⓑ Sometimes mail comes by truck.

   Ⓒ Men on horses once delivered the mail.

   Ⓓ Getting the mail is a lot of fun.

9. **What happens after the mail arrives at the post office?**

   Ⓐ It is sorted by workers.

   Ⓑ It is taken out of your mailbox.

   Ⓒ It is carried on horses.

   Ⓓ It comes in huge trucks.

10. **Mail can come by _____ or by truck.**

   Ⓐ trane

   Ⓑ traine

   Ⓒ train

   Ⓓ trayn

Name _____

11. I hope the mail carrier will come this _____.

    Ⓐ way

    Ⓑ wai

    Ⓒ wa

    Ⓓ waye

12. She will _____ the mail at noon today.

    Ⓐ bringg

    Ⓑ bing

    Ⓒ brig

    Ⓓ bring

13. The riders rode their horses at _____.

    Ⓐ night

    Ⓑ nite

    Ⓒ nigt

    Ⓓ niht

Name _____

Student Evaluation Chart

TESTED SKILLS	Number Correct	Percent Correct
Vocabulary	/5	%
Context clues, 1, 2, 4		
Word Parts: Plural Endings -s and -es, 3		
Antonyms, 5		
Reading Comprehension	/4	%
Author's Purpose, 6, 7		
Summarize: fact and opinion, 8, 9		
Phonics	/4	%
Long /ā/ay, ai, 10, 11		
Initial and final blends, 12		
Long /ī/, igh, ie, y, 13		
Total Weekly Test Score	/13	%

ANSWER KEY
1. D; 2. C; 3. B; 4. A; 5. C; 6. A; 7. B; 8. D; 9. A; 10.C; 11.A; 12.D; 13.A

Our Great Cook

My dad is a great cook. Even a bowl of oatmeal made by Dad is great. I love breakfast. We usually have toast from a fresh loaf of bread.

The best day is Sunday. Dad makes a large feast for us. He makes a roast. He makes lots of things to go with it. We eat midday on Sundays. It is a lot of fun.

Dad told us that once he was a waiter. He was not very good. He was too slow. But then they let him cook. He was great! The cook would explain things to Dad. Dad got it right away. So now he cooks at home. I am glad Dad was a bad waiter. Now he is a great cook! And he shows us what to do. I can't wait to cook like Dad!

Name _____

Directions: Fill in the circle next to the best answer.

1. **What does *feast* mean in the sentence below?**

   Dad cooks us a *feast*.

   ⓐ a piece of toast

   ⓑ a big meal

   ⓒ oatmeal

   ⓓ a small breakfast

2. **Which word means the same as *large*?**

   ⓐ big

   ⓑ small

   ⓒ tiny

   ⓓ slow

3. **What time is it when it is *midday*?**

   ⓐ midnight

   ⓑ morning

   ⓒ breakfast

   ⓓ noon

4. **Why is Sunday the best day?**

   ⓐ because Dad makes oatmeal

   ⓑ because there is no school

   ⓒ because Dad makes fresh bread

   ⓓ because Dad's feast is so good

Name _____

5. **Why is the writer glad that Dad was a bad waiter?**

Ⓐ because the writer doesn't like waiters

Ⓑ because Dad was too busy

Ⓒ because Dad learned to be a good cook

Ⓓ because Dad makes good roasts

6. **Dad made us a fresh _____ of bread.**

Ⓐ loff

Ⓑ loaf

Ⓒ lof

Ⓓ lowf

7. **He will _____ us how to cook.**

Ⓐ shoe

Ⓑ sho

Ⓒ show

Ⓓ showe

8. **Which word is spelled correctly?**

Ⓐ toeld

Ⓑ toled

Ⓒ told

Ⓓ towld

Grade 3 • Unit 3 • Week 1

Student Evaluation Chart

TESTED SKILLS	Number Correct	Percent Correct
Vocabulary	/3	%
Context clues, 1, 3		
Synonyms, 2		
Reading Comprehension	/2	%
Make inferences, 4, 5		
Phonics	/3	%
Long /ō/oa, ow, oe, 6, 7, 8		
Total Weekly Test Score	/8	%

ANSWER KEY
1. B; 2. A; 3. D; 4. D; 5. C; 6. B; 7. C; 8. C

© Macmillan/McGraw-Hill

Mitch Goes to Lunch

It was midday and just before lunchtime. Mitch Roan looked at his watch. "Time for lunch!" he thought. He reached for his coat. He walked out of his office and down the hall. Then he ran to catch the elevator. Soon the doors closed and he was gone.

Lee Patch yelled, "The coast is clear!" Everyone ran out into the hallway. "Is everything ready?" asked Deb Branch. "I have it all under control," boasted Lee Patch.

Soon Mitch was on his way back to his office. He walked down the hallway. Everything was quiet. "Where is everyone?" thought Mitch. He looked into each office. No one was there. The door to his office was closed. "That is strange," he thought. "It was open when I left for lunch." Mitch reached for the door. The light switch was off. Then he heard, "Happy Birthday!" It was a party for Mitch! What an unexpected treat!

Name _____

Directions: Fill in the circle next to the best answer.

1. **What is the meaning of the word *boasted*?**

   Ⓐ bragged

   Ⓑ told

   Ⓒ complained

   Ⓓ asked

2. **Mitch went back to his _____ after lunch.**

   Ⓐ coast

   Ⓑ office

   Ⓒ trust

   Ⓓ latch

3. **What does *coast is clear* mean in the sentence below?**

   "You can come out now! The <u>coast is clear!</u>"

   Ⓐ It is fun.

   Ⓑ It is quiet.

   Ⓒ It is dark.

   Ⓓ It is safe.

4. **In the sentence below which word means the same as** *closed*?

> The door to his office was <u>closed</u>.

Ⓐ shut

Ⓑ open

Ⓒ down

Ⓓ right

5. **What does** *midday* **mean in the sentence below?**

> It was <u>midday</u> and just before lunchtime.

Ⓐ late

Ⓑ morning

Ⓒ noon

Ⓓ midnight

6. **Where does the story take place?**

Ⓐ in an elevator

Ⓑ outside

Ⓒ at a play

Ⓓ in an office building

7. **What happened when Mitch came back from lunch?**

Ⓐ There was someone in the elevator.

Ⓑ There were three people working with him.

Ⓒ There was a surprise party for him.

Ⓓ There was a sandwich waiting for him.

8. **How do you think Mitch felt about his party?**

   Ⓐ scared

   Ⓑ happy

   Ⓒ angry

   Ⓓ tired

9. **Why did Lee Patch say "the coast is clear?"**

   Ⓐ because Mitch had left

   Ⓑ because it was lunchtime

   Ⓒ because it was midday

   Ⓓ because he liked Mitch

10. **Midday is a good time for _____ .**

   Ⓐ luch

   Ⓑ luntch

   Ⓒ lunh

   Ⓓ lunch

Name _____

11. He looked at his _____ to tell the time.
   Ⓐ wach
   Ⓑ watch
   Ⓒ wath
   Ⓓ wotch

12. Mitch put on his _____ before he went out.
   Ⓐ coat
   Ⓑ cote
   Ⓒ cowt
   Ⓓ coet

13. He had a _____ of soup for lunch.
   Ⓐ bole
   Ⓑ boal
   Ⓒ bowl
   Ⓓ boll

Name _____

Student Evaluation Chart

TESTED SKILLS	Number Correct	Percent Correct
Vocabulary	/5	%
Context clues, 2, 3		
Unfamiliar words, 1		
Synonyms, 4, 5		
Reading Comprehension	/4	%
Plot and setting, 6, 7		
Make inferences, 8, 9		
Phonics	/4	%
Digraphs /ch/ ch, tch, 10, 11		
Long /ō/oa, ow, oe, 12, 13		
Total Weekly Test Score	/13	%

ANSWER KEY
1. A; 2. B; 3. D; 4. A; 5. C; 6. D; 7. C; 8. B; 9. A; 10.D; 11.B; 12.A; 13.C

Rafting on the River

Last summer I went rafting on a river. I went with my dad and my brother Theo. Theo is thirteen. I think he started rafting when he was seven. But it was my first time. We left early and there was a chill in the air. We each wore floats in the raft. They were to protect us if we fell in. They felt like they were 50 pounds!

At first we felt rocks beneath the raft. Then we felt a thump. We had hit white water! White water runs very fast. The raft bumped all over the rocks. Water sprayed in like raindrops. I almost fell out! We paddled to shore and then my dad drained the raft. I was so happy to be on dry land. And it was lunchtime. My mom met us and we had lunch beneath the trees. I thought that was the best part of the day!

Name _____

Directions: Fill in the circle next to the best answer.

1. **There were rocks _____ the water.**
   - Ⓐ protect
   - Ⓑ beneath
   - Ⓒ over
   - Ⓓ left

2. **Which meaning of *pounds* is correct in the sentence below?**

They felt like they were 50 <u>pounds</u>!

   - Ⓐ units of money
   - Ⓑ hits
   - Ⓒ units of weight
   - Ⓓ strikes

3. **The float will _____ you if you fall in.**
   - Ⓐ pretect
   - Ⓑ under
   - Ⓒ over
   - Ⓓ protect

4. **What was the effect of white water on the raft?**
   - Ⓐ It caused water to pour in.
   - Ⓑ It caused the boy to fall out.
   - Ⓒ It caused the mom to meet them.
   - Ⓓ It caused the rocks to fall in.

© Macmillan/McGraw-Hill

Name _____

5. **What happens if you do not wear a float on a raft?**

Ⓐ You are not warm.

Ⓑ You are not thirteen.

Ⓒ You do not travel as fast.

Ⓓ You are not safe.

6. **Water sprayed in like _____ .**

Ⓐ raindrops

Ⓑ snowflakes

Ⓒ thunder

Ⓓ a hose

7. **_____ water runs very fast.**

Ⓐ Wite

Ⓑ White

Ⓒ Whit

Ⓓ Whyte

8. **Which word is spelled correctly?**

Ⓐ thmp

Ⓑ thump

Ⓒ tump

Ⓓ thompp

Name _____

Student Evaluation Chart

TESTED SKILLS	Number Correct	Percent Correct
Vocabulary	/3	%
Context clues, 1, 3		
Multiple meaning words, 2		
Reading Comprehension	/2	%
Cause and effect, 4, 5		
Phonics	/2	%
Digraphs /th/th, /hw/wh, 7, 8		
Structural Analysis	/1	%
Multisyllable words: closed syllables, with blends and digraphs, 6		
Total Weekly Test Score	/8	%

ANSWER KEY
1. B; 2. C; 3. D; 4. A; 5. D; 6. A; 7. B; 8. B

My Visit to the Museum

Have you ever been to a natural history museum? There are amazing things to see there. Once I had a chance to visit the museum in New York City. That place was huge! I never imagined it would be so large. I think it was seven floors. Every floor had something great to see.

It was hard to decide where to go first. I could see dinosaur bones or learn about ancient cities. I could see lots of animals too. I decided to start on the first floor but then changed my mind.

I think I liked the huge animals best. They looked so real! I looked at the animals up close. I could almost see the mist in the trees. But there was no real danger. It was so nice to be at the museum. I think I will go back soon.

Name _____

Directions: Fill in the circle next to the best answer.

1. **What does *ancient* mean in the sentence below?**

   > You can learn about ancient cities from long ago.

   Ⓐ local

   Ⓑ scary

   Ⓒ very old

   Ⓓ important

2. **There were so many _____ things to see.**

   Ⓐ local

   Ⓑ tilted

   Ⓒ imagined

   Ⓓ amazing

3. **I thought I could see the _____ in the trees.**

   Ⓐ missed

   Ⓑ misst

   Ⓒ mist

   Ⓓ miset

4. **How do you know the writer liked the museum?**

   Ⓐ Because it was ancient.

   Ⓑ Because there are many amazing things to see.

   Ⓒ Because the animals were dangerous.

   Ⓓ Because there were seven floors.

5. **Why might it be hard to decide where to start in the museum?**

   Ⓐ Because the animals are huge.

   Ⓑ Because the museum is so large.

   Ⓒ Because it is dangerous.

   Ⓓ Because there is mist.

6. **You could see the animals, but there was no real ___ .**

   Ⓐ danger

   Ⓑ danjer

   Ⓒ dangr

   Ⓓ danjur

7. **It was _____ to see the animals in the museum.**

   Ⓐ nice

   Ⓑ nic

   Ⓒ nise

   Ⓓ nyce

8. **This museum was the _____ one I ever saw.**

   Ⓐ bigest

   Ⓑ biggist

   Ⓒ bigger

   Ⓓ biggest

© Macmillan/McGraw-Hill

Name _____

Student Evaluation Chart

TESTED SKILLS	Number Correct	Percent Correct
Vocabulary	/3	%
Context clues, 1, 2		
Homophones, 3		
Reading Comprehension	/2	%
Make Inferences, 4, 5		
Phonics	/2	%
Soft consonants /s/c, /j/g, g(e), 6, 7		
Structural Analysis	/1	%
Comparative Suffixes: –er, –est, 8		
Total Weekly Test Score	/8	%

ANSWER KEY
1. C; 2. D; 3. C; 4. B; 5. B; 6. A; 7. A; 8. D

A Project About Me

This year in art class, we made projects about us. We all chose whatever we wanted to do. My idea was to make a collage.

First, I gathered lots of photos. Each photo was from a different year of my life. Then I put them on a large sheet of paper. Next, I imagined what I would look like when I was older. I made some sketches beneath the photos. I used a brush and paint to fill in my sketches. It took me a while to finish. Finally it was done. It told the complete story of my life. It was really nice.

It was amazing to see all of my classmates' art projects. Some of them were huge! My friend boasted that hers was the largest. But that didn't matter. I liked them all!

Name _____

Directions: Fill in the circle next to the best answer.

1. **What does *gathered* mean in the sentence below?**

I <u>gathered</u> lots of photos.

   Ⓐ painted

   Ⓑ traced

   Ⓒ copied

   Ⓓ collected

2. **There were so many _____ projects!**

   Ⓐ amazing

   Ⓑ protected

   Ⓒ tilted

   Ⓓ tired

3. **What does *beneath* mean in the sentence below?**

The sketches were <u>beneath</u> the photos on the paper.

   Ⓐ next to

   Ⓑ over

   Ⓒ under

   Ⓓ above

4. If your friend has *boasted* it means she has _____ .

Ⓐ worked

Ⓑ bragged

Ⓒ helped

Ⓓ understood

5. Which word means the same as *huge*?

Ⓐ large

Ⓑ tiny

Ⓒ fancy

Ⓓ close

6. What did the writer do FIRST?

Ⓐ cut out pictures

Ⓑ gather photos

Ⓒ draw sketches

Ⓓ paint in the sketches

7. What did the writer do AFTER he drew sketches?

Ⓐ painted in the sketches

Ⓑ gathered photos

Ⓒ cut out the sketches

Ⓓ cut up the photos

© Macmillan/McGraw-Hill

8. **Why did the writer only imagine what he or she would look like as an older person?**

   Ⓐ Because there was not enough time.

   Ⓑ Because there were too many photos.

   Ⓒ Because the sketches needed to be painted.

   Ⓓ Because he or she couldn't really know.

9. **Where did the writer get to see everyone's art project?**

   Ⓐ at home

   Ⓑ in art class

   Ⓒ at a play

   Ⓓ on a train

10. **I use a _____ to help me paint.**

    Ⓐ brus

    Ⓑ bruh

    Ⓒ bruph

    Ⓓ brush

11. I used a _____ of myself in my art project.

    Ⓐ photo

    Ⓑ foto

    Ⓒ phoeto

    Ⓓ poto

12. Your project is really ____ .

    Ⓐ nise

    Ⓑ nic

    Ⓒ nice

    Ⓓ nis

13. What a _____ picture!

    Ⓐ large

    Ⓑ larg

    Ⓒ lardge

    Ⓓ larg

Grade 3 • Unit 3 • Week 5

Student Evaluation Chart

TESTED SKILLS	Number Correct	Percent Correct
Vocabulary	/5	%
Context clues, 1, 2, 3, 4,		
Synonyms, 5		
Reading Comprehension	/4	%
Sequence, 6, 7		
Make Inferences, 8		
Plot and Setting, 9		
Phonics	/4	%
Digraphs /sh/sh, /ph/ph, 10, 11		
Soft consonants /s/c, /j/g, g(e), 12, 13		
Total Weekly Test Score	/13	%

ANSWER KEY
1. D; 2. A; 3. C; 4. B; 5. A; 6. B; 7. A; 8. D; 9. B; 10.D; 11.A; 12.C; 13.A

Funny Shapes

"Help me make the batter, Ken," said Meg. "We all want to make lots of shapes." Ken stood at the table. Meg had to stand on a chair. "These will be splendid" said Meg. "Everybody will want to eat more than three."

"The recipe says to add two tbs. of water," said Ken.

Kate and Tad came to help. They lived next door. "Now we roll the batter," said Meg. "The batter has to be flat. It has to be as flat as a pancake." The children cut different shapes from the batter. They cut boats and trains. They cut sad and happy faces. "These will give everybody a thrill," Meg said.

The shapes baked. Meg watched the clock. Kate watched the flat cookies rise. Ken took them from the oven. Meg put them on a plate.

Then the children put frosting on the shapes. Some frosting was red. Some was black. Tad put black stripes on a cat shape. They all scraped the frosting bowl. They licked their fingers. Then Tad and Kate washed the pans. "Don't eat all of the funny shapes," Meg smiled. "We want to save some for later."

Name _____

Directions: Fill in the circle next to the best answer.

1. **What does *recipe* mean in the sentence below?**

   > The recipe says to add two tbs. of water.

   Ⓐ pans

   Ⓑ numbers

   Ⓒ directions

   Ⓓ shapes

2. **What does *rise* mean in the story?**

   Ⓐ to scream

   Ⓑ to get smaller

   Ⓒ to get lower

   Ⓓ to get higher

3. **What does *flat as a pancake* mean in the story?**

   Ⓐ very, very flat

   Ⓑ very, very soft

   Ⓒ very, very small

   Ⓓ very, very big

4. **How are all the characters in the story alike?**

   Ⓐ They are all in the same family.

   Ⓑ They all like pets.

   Ⓒ They are all the same age.

   Ⓓ They all like baking.

Name _____

5. **What can you infer about Meg?**

   Ⓐ Meg is older than Ken.

   Ⓑ Meg is shorter than the others.

   Ⓒ Meg is older than Kate.

   Ⓓ Meg doesn't like to bake.

6. **Which word is spelled correctly?**

   Ⓐ splesh

   Ⓑ spleesh

   Ⓒ splush

   Ⓓ splash

7. **Which word completes this sentence?**

Molly got a _____ on her leg from the broken fence.

   Ⓐ scream

   Ⓑ screw

   Ⓒ scratch

   Ⓓ scrawl

8. **Which abbreviation for *tablespoon* is correct?**

   Ⓐ tssps.

   Ⓑ tb.

   Ⓒ tbs.

   Ⓓ lb.

Name _____

Student Evaluation Chart

TESTED SKILLS	Number Correct	Percent Correct
Vocabulary	/3	%
Context clues, 1, 2		
Idioms, 3		
Reading Comprehension	/2	%
Make Inferences: Compare and contrast, 4, 5		
Phonics	/2	%
Triple blends, 6, 7		
Structural Analysis	/1	%
Abbreviations, 8		
Total Weekly Test Score	/8	%

ANSWER KEY
1. C; 2. D; 3. A; 4. D; 5. B; 6. D; 7. C; 8. C

Splendid Friends

Dan and Beth did not get along. Dan liked to run. Beth liked to play tennis.

When Dan ran around the block, Beth's dog barked. When Beth played tennis, the sound of the ball was too loud for Dan. The two children did not speak when they passed each other on the street.

One day the knot on Dan's shoe came loose. He tripped and hurt his knee. The next day Beth scraped her knuckles. Then she hurt her wrist. Now Dan could not run. Beth could not play tennis.

Dan put a wrap around his knee. Beth put a wrap around her wrist. Dan said, "I will knock on Beth's door." Beth said, "Hello, Dan. I'll help you to make your knee strong again. You can help me make my wrist strong."

Beth helped Dan stretch his knee. Soon he could rise from a chair without pain. Dan helped Beth move her wrist. The two children grew strong. They got to know each other and became splendid friends. They beamed at each other.

"Dan, we were wrong not to be friends," said Beth. Dan gave a chuckle.

In a month, Dan earned a trophy in running. Beth earned a trophy in tennis.

Name _____

Directions: Fill in the circle next to the best answer.

1. **What does the term *get along* mean in the sentence?**

   | The two children were angry and did not *get along*. |

   Ⓐ live on the same street

   Ⓑ go to the same school

   Ⓒ feel friendly to each other

   Ⓓ practice sports together

2. **What does the word *beamed* mean in the sentence?**

   | The two happy friends *beamed* at each other. |

   Ⓐ threw things

   Ⓑ frowned

   Ⓒ shined a light

   Ⓓ smiled widely

3. **What does the word *block* mean in the sentence?**

   | When Dan ran around the *block,* Beth's dog barked. |

   Ⓐ a children's toy

   Ⓑ an area with streets on each side

   Ⓒ to keep from passing, as a football player

   Ⓓ to fill a passageway up and keep it closed

© Macmillan/McGraw-Hill

Name _____

4. **Which word completes the sentence?**

> "You ran a _____ race," said Dan's mother.

Ⓐ splendor

Ⓑ splendid

Ⓒ splashy

Ⓓ split

5. **Which word means "move from a lower position to a higher position"?**

Ⓐ wrap

Ⓑ flatten

Ⓒ rise

Ⓓ wring

6. **What conclusion can you draw about Beth and Dan?**

   Ⓐ They are both clumsy.

   Ⓑ They both have sports skills.

   Ⓒ They both have pets.

   Ⓓ They are brother and sister.

7. **What other conclusion can you draw about Beth and Dan?**

   Ⓐ They live near each other.

   Ⓑ They go to the same school.

   Ⓒ They play other sports, too.

   Ⓓ They have earned many medals.

8. **How is Dan different from Beth?**

   Ⓐ Dan is older.

   Ⓑ Dan is a runner.

   Ⓒ Dan never wins medals.

   Ⓓ Dan doesn't like dogs.

9. **How are Dan and Beth alike?**

   Ⓐ They both exercise by doing sports.

   Ⓑ They are both the same age.

   Ⓒ They play the same sports.

   Ⓓ They compete against each other.

10. Which word is spelled correctly?

Ⓐ rist

Ⓑ wriste

Ⓒ riste

Ⓓ wrist

11. Which word completes the sentence?

> Dan tied a tight _____ in his shoelace.

Ⓐ knot

Ⓑ knee

Ⓒ knit

Ⓓ knock

12. Which word is spelled correctly?

Ⓐ skraped

Ⓑ scrapt

Ⓒ skrapt

Ⓓ scraped

13. I'll help you to make your knee _____ again.

Ⓐ srong

Ⓑ strong

Ⓒ stong

Ⓓ stronge

Grade 3 • Unit 4 • Week 2

Student Evaluation Chart

TESTED SKILLS	Number Correct	Percent Correct
Vocabulary	/5	%
Context clues, 1, 2, 4, 5		
Multiple-meaning words, 3		
Reading Comprehension	/4	%
Make inferences and analyze: draw conclusions, 6, 7		
Make inferences and analyze: compare and contrast, 8, 9		
Phonics	/4	%
Silent consonants, (kn, wr), 10, 11		
Triple blends, 12, 13		
Total Weekly Test Score	/13	%

ANSWER KEY
1. C; 2. D; 3. B; 4. B; 5. C; 6. B; 7. A; 8. B; 9. A; 10. D; 11. A; 12. D; 13. B

Mark and Matt

Mark the lark was looking for bugs to eat. It was almost dusk. He had to eat and then sleep. He flew to where two streams met. Matt the bat flew down nearby.

"What are you doing here?" asked Mark. "You're a bat. You hunt for food after dark."

"Oh, I was hungry for bugs today. I didn't want to wait for dark," said Matt. "Why are you here? You're a bird. You look for food during the day. You should be in your nest by now."

Mark lifted his beak. Drops of liquid dripped from his mouth. "Well, pardon me," he said. "I like the dusk. I like this time between day and dark. There is a nice supply of bugs to eat. It's not hard to find food."

Matt said, "Shhh, there's the falcon. He hunts at dusk. I don't want to be his dinner. We have to hide."

Mark and Matt hid in the marsh. The wetlands had many common plants and grass that could hide them. The last rays of sun beamed down. The falcon left. "This is a good time for us to start meeting," said Mark, "between my day and your dark. Remember, see you tomorrow."

Name _____

Directions: Fill in the circle next to the best answer.

1. **What does *dusk* mean in the sentence?**

   > Some birds like to hunt at *dusk* when the sun sets.

   Ⓐ a cloudy time

   Ⓑ nighttime

   Ⓒ just before dawn

   Ⓓ between day and dark

2. **Which word completes the sentence?**

   > The animals drank at the _____.

   Ⓐ stripes

   Ⓑ screams

   Ⓒ streams

   Ⓓ straws

3. **How are Matt and Mark alike?**

   Ⓐ They both fly and eat bugs.

   Ⓑ They both hunt in daylight.

   Ⓒ They both dislike the dusk.

   Ⓓ They both hunt after dark.

4. **How is Matt the bat different from Mark the lark?**

   Ⓐ He isn't afraid of the falcon.

   Ⓑ He usually hunts for food after dark.

   Ⓒ He is bigger and stronger than Mark.

   Ⓓ He doesn't like to fly.

5. **Which words are combined in the underlined contraction in the sentence?**

> I <u>don't</u> want to be the falcon's food.

Ⓐ did not

Ⓑ can not

Ⓒ will not

Ⓓ do not

6. **Which word is spelled correctly?**

Ⓐ sart

Ⓑ startt

Ⓒ start

Ⓓ starrt

7. **Which word completes the sentence?**

> Mark and Matt hid in the _____ from the falcon.

Ⓐ mart

Ⓑ cart

Ⓒ marsh

Ⓓ harsh

8. **Which word is spelled correctly?**

Ⓐ common

Ⓑ kommen

Ⓒ kommon

Ⓓ comon

© Macmillan/McGraw-Hill

Name _____

Student Evaluation Chart

TESTED SKILLS	Number Correct	Percent Correct
Vocabulary	/3	%
Context clues, 1, 2		
Contractions, 5		
Reading Comprehension	/2	%
Compare and contrast, 3, 4		
Phonics	/3	%
r-controlled vowel (ar), 6, 7		
Multisyllable words (-en, -on), 8		
Total Weekly Test Score	/8	%

ANSWER KEY
1. D; 2. C; 3. A; 4. B; 5. D; 6. C; 7. C; 8. A

The Storm

Barb and Norm did their chores. They took out the garbage. They mowed the grass. "Let's paint the porch," said Barb. "It will be a fun project!"

"I have many talents, such as fixing the car," said Norm. "But painting is not one of them. Besides, today isn't a good day to paint. It will storm later."

Barb ignored Norm. She didn't agree with him about the storm. She collected brushes and cans of paint. She put newspapers on the porch. She mixed the paint. "I'll have to start soon," she said. "I'll paint all morning."

"Bart and I have to go to the store," said Norm. "I need dog shampoo." Norm and Bart the dog walked to the store. When they came out, the sky was dark. "C'mon, Bart, it's going to storm. We have to get home," said Norm. Norm and Bart ran down the street.

Norm saw Barb on the porch. He helped her move the paint cans inside the house. Soon the rain started. Bart barked. He ran around in the rain. He pulled Norm and Barb with him. They laughed at Bart. They all got wet.

Name _____

Directions: Fill in the circle next to the best answer.

1. **What does the word *collected* mean in the story?**
   - Ⓐ paid for
   - Ⓑ hid
   - Ⓒ gathered together
   - Ⓓ put away

2. **What does the word *chores* mean in the story?**
   - Ⓐ tasks
   - Ⓑ games
   - Ⓒ studies
   - Ⓓ songs

3. **What does the word *talents* mean in the story?**
   - Ⓐ wishes
   - Ⓑ tools
   - Ⓒ videos
   - Ⓓ skills

4. **What is the author's purpose in this story?**
   - Ⓐ to teach
   - Ⓑ to inform
   - Ⓒ to entertain
   - Ⓓ to persuade

© Macmillan/McGraw-Hill

5. **How does the author carry out his purpose in this story?**

Ⓐ by describing how to give Bart a bath

Ⓑ by describing Barb's and Norm's day

Ⓒ by persuading readers to avoid storms

Ⓓ by showing how Barb gets ready to paint

6. **Which word is spelled correctly?**

Ⓐ before

Ⓑ befor

Ⓒ beforr

Ⓓ befour

7. **Why did Norm think it was not a good day to paint?**

Ⓐ There was no more paint.

Ⓑ It was too much of a chore.

Ⓒ It was going to storm later.

Ⓓ The porch did not need to be painted.

8. **Which two words make up the underlined contraction in the sentence?**

"Let's paint the porch," said Barb.

Ⓐ You will

Ⓑ Let us

Ⓒ We will

Ⓓ I can

Grade 3 • Unit 4 • Week 4

Student Evaluation Chart

TESTED SKILLS	Number Correct	Percent Correct
Vocabulary	/3	%
Context clues, 1, 2		
Context clues, Examples, 3		
Reading Comprehension	/2	%
Author's purpose, 4, 5		
Phonics	/2	%
r-controlled vowel (or), 6, 7		
Sructural Analysis	/1	%
Contractions, 8		
Total Weekly Test Score	/8	%

ANSWER KEY
1. C; 2. A; 3. D; 4. C; 5. B; 6. A; 7. C; 8. B

A Day in the Woods

"We have walked so far," sighed Burt. "My knee is stiff. Can't we rest in this shady place? I wish we had gone to the movies."

"It's shadier over there where there are more trees," said Dora. They sat near the stream. "Look, if you stir the water, you can see tiny fish," said Dora. "I wonder what they are."

"I'm so bored," whined Burt. All at once he slipped and fell into the water.

"Wring your shirt out," laughed Dora. "I'll bet you're not bored any more."

As the sun beamed down, Burt perked up. He found a red flower.

"You think being outside is such a chore," laughed Dora. "But I think it's splendid. I love to see all the trees and birds and animals. Let's climb this hill and see what is up there."

The hill was slippery. They kept sliding back down. Their pants were covered with dirt. "Mom is going to be mad," said Burt. "She won't ignore this." Some rocks rolled down the hill and made a splash in the stream.

"Now I'm tired, too," said Dora. The two children collected their backpacks and headed for home.

Name _____

Directions: Fill in the circle next to the best answer.

1. **The tall tree was _____ than the short tree.**

   Ⓐ shady

   Ⓑ shade

   Ⓒ shadiest

   Ⓓ shadier

2. **What does the word *chore* mean in the sentence?**

Burt thought walking in the woods was a *chore* and wished he were at the movies.

   Ⓐ boring or hard activity

   Ⓑ exciting activity

   Ⓒ scary activity

   Ⓓ strange activity

3. **Why did Burt perk up?**

   Ⓐ He fell into the water.

   Ⓑ The sun beamed down and he found a flower.

   Ⓒ He went to the movies.

   Ⓓ He rolled down the hill.

Name _____

4. **What does *wring* mean in the story?**

   Ⓐ twist out

   Ⓑ shake

   Ⓒ iron

   Ⓓ soak

5. **"I think it's _____ to be in the great outdoors,"**
   laughed Dora.

   Ⓐ splashy

   Ⓑ splattered

   Ⓒ splendid

   Ⓓ splintered

6. **What MOST likely caused the hillside to be slippery?**

   Ⓐ Animals have torn up the grass.

   Ⓑ It has rained recently.

   Ⓒ There are no trees to hold on to.

   Ⓓ It is covered with flat stones.

7. **When the children get home, what will their mother**
   MOST likely do?

   Ⓐ She will tell them they have missed dinner.

   Ⓑ She will ask them how school was that day.

   Ⓒ She will ask them to change into different clothes.

   Ⓓ She will tell them not to go back to the woods.

8. **How is Dora different from Burt?**

Ⓐ She is good at climbing hills.

Ⓑ She knows the names of many fish.

Ⓒ She doesn't like doing chores.

Ⓓ She enjoys being outside in the woods.

9. **What conclusion can you draw about Burt from the story?**

Ⓐ He likes to go to the movies.

Ⓑ He likes to count fish in the stream.

Ⓒ He likes to climb slippery hills.

Ⓓ He likes to be outdoors in the woods.

10. **Which word is spelled correctly?**

Ⓐ derty

Ⓑ dirtie

Ⓒ dirty

Ⓓ durty

11. **Which word is spelled incorrectly?**

Ⓐ shirt

Ⓑ turn

Ⓒ girl

Ⓓ burd

12. Which word completes the sentence?

Let's get inside before it starts to _____.

Ⓐ storm

Ⓑ score

Ⓒ store

Ⓓ stork

13. Which word completes the sentence?

My brother hurt his _____ when he fell over a tree root.

Ⓐ knot

Ⓑ knee

Ⓒ knock

Ⓓ knife

Name _____

Student Evaluation Chart

TESTED SKILLS	Number Correct	Percent Correct
Vocabulary	/5	%
Comparatives and Superlatives, 1		
Context Clues, 2, 3, 4, 5		
Comprehension	/4	%
Make and confirm predictions, 6, 7		
Compare and contrast, 8		
Draw conclusions, 9		
Phonics	/4	%
r-controlled vowels (or, er, ir, ur): 10, 11, 12		
Silent Consonants, 13		
Total Weekly Test Score	/13	%

ANSWER KEY
1. D; 2. A; 3. B; 4. A; 5. C; 6. B; 7. C; 8. D; 9. A; 10. C; 11. D; 12. A; 13. B

Abe Is a Good Cook

"Where are the frozen fries?" said Lee. She owned the diner. Most people liked to eat fries. Where were the fries?

Customers came in all day. They wanted meals. One family had a tiny baby. "Abe, get a high chair," said Lee. "Abe, get a bib," said Lee.

Abe got a high chair for the baby. He got a bib. "I found the fries," he said. "Now we won't run out." Lee and Abe turned on the music. Kids from the nearby school came in. They drank milk. They ate burgers. Some did their homework at the tables.

Everything was done in order. First, people gave their order. They told Lee what they wanted to eat. Next, the cooks made the meals. Third, the staff served the meals. Last, people paid and left.

Lee talked to the people. They talked to her. They liked Lee. They liked the diner. They were good customers.

Abe was a cook. He made oatmeal. He made toast. He liked to bake pies and cakes. Most of all, he liked to make French fries. He didn't even mind cleaning up. Abe was a good cook. Maybe he would run his own diner someday.

Name _____

Directions: Fill in the circle next to the best answer.

1. **Which does the word *nearby* mean in the story?**
   - Ⓐ far away
   - Ⓑ brick
   - Ⓒ close
   - Ⓓ old

2. **Which word completes the sentence?**

   | The baby needs a _____ chair for his size. |

   - Ⓐ big
   - Ⓑ special
   - Ⓒ painted
   - Ⓓ clean

3. **Which word in the sentence is a compound word?**

   | The kids did homework while other customers ate. |

   - Ⓐ kids
   - Ⓑ homework
   - Ⓒ other
   - Ⓓ customers

4. **Which actions are in sequence?**
   - Ⓐ pies and cakes are baked
   - Ⓑ food is frozen for later use
   - Ⓒ customers talk to Lee
   - Ⓓ people are served and then they pay

5. **Which action takes place after people order food?**

Ⓐ The cooks make the meals.

Ⓑ Customers pay and leave.

Ⓒ Customers say what they want to eat.

Ⓓ Meals are served to customers.

6. **Which word is spelled correctly?**

Ⓐ musick

Ⓑ musck

Ⓒ music

Ⓓ museik

7. **Which word is spelled incorrectly?**

Ⓐ frozzen

Ⓑ diner

Ⓒ silent

Ⓓ baby

8. **The word <u>tiny</u> is an example of _____ ?**

Ⓐ a compound word

Ⓑ a closed-syllable word

Ⓒ a contraction

Ⓓ an open-syllable word

Name _____

Grade 3 • Unit 5 • Week 1

Student Evaluation Chart

TESTED SKILLS	Number Correct	Percent Correct
Vocabulary	/3	%
Context, 1, 2		
Compound words, 3		
Reading Comprehension	/2	%
Summarize: sequence, 4, 5		
Phonics	/3	%
Open syllables: long vowels, 6, 7, 8		
Total Weekly Test Score	/8	%

ANSWER KEY
1. C; 2. B; 3. B; 4. D; 5. A; 6. C; 7. A; 8. D

Childhood Book

Ed and Jane ran in the park. Jane ran through the brook. Ed ran after her.

"Jane, let's write a book," said Ed. "You can write. I can draw. I want to write something important and special. I want to do something that stands out."

"Let's write about our childhood," said Jane. "We lived in many towns. We went to many schools. I liked the tiny home in Ohio. There was a diner on the street. It served good apple cider. I liked that home. It was hard to say goodbye."

"How did we survive the third grade?" laughed Ed. "Oh, the big kids! They told us to get out of the park. They told us we were breaking the laws. What laws?"

"But we stood as one," said Jane. "We were united. We didn't let them scare us. And they went away."

"Open your notebook," said Ed. "We have to take notes. I'll take notes on the people we met. You take notes on the places we lived."

"Yes," said Jane. "But first, let's get something to eat. I'm hungry and the diner has a good cook."

Name _____

Directions: Fill in the circle next to the best answer.

1. **What does the word _united_ mean in the passage?**

We were _united_. We stood as one.

   Ⓐ scared

   Ⓑ standing up

   Ⓒ acting together as one

   Ⓓ running away

2. **What does the word _childhood_ mean in the sentence?**

Jane and Ed remembered their _childhood_ in third grade.

   Ⓐ birthdays

   Ⓑ tests

   Ⓒ early years

   Ⓓ behavior

3. **Which of these words does not belong in the same word family?**

   Ⓐ notebook

   Ⓑ footprint

   Ⓒ bookcase

   Ⓓ cookbook

Name _____

4. **What does the word *special* mean in the sentence?**

> I want to do something *special*. I want to do
> something that stands out.

Ⓐ unusual, different

Ⓑ expensive

Ⓒ hard

Ⓓ easy

5. **Which of these words is NOT a compound word?**

Ⓐ barefoot

Ⓑ bookbag

Ⓒ something

Ⓓ important

6. **What is the effect of Ed wanting to write a book?**

Ⓐ Ed and Jane run in the park.

Ⓑ Ed and Jane play good music.

Ⓒ Ed and Jane talk about their childhood.

Ⓓ Ed and Jane buy cookies.

7. **What causes the big kids to leave Ed and Jane alone?**

Ⓐ The two children run away.

Ⓑ The two children laugh at them.

Ⓒ The two children unite as one.

Ⓓ The two children show them their book.

8. **What do Ed and Jane do first to get ready to write their book?**

   Ⓐ They run through the brook.

   Ⓑ They take notes in a notebook.

   Ⓒ They talk about their childhood.

   Ⓓ They take off their shoes.

9. **What do Ed and Jane do AFTER they open their notebooks?**

   Ⓐ They decide to get something to eat.

   Ⓑ They run through the brook.

   Ⓒ They talk about the big kids.

   Ⓓ They move to Ohio.

10. **Which word completes the sentence?**

   Ed and Jane ran through the _____.

   Ⓐ break

   Ⓑ brook

   Ⓒ book

   Ⓓ broke

11. **What is the name of a riding vehicle with only *one* wheel?**

   Ⓐ tricycle

   Ⓑ bicycle

   Ⓒ unicycle

   Ⓓ recycle

© Macmillan/McGraw-Hill

Name _____

12. Which word is spelled correctly?

 Ⓐ cider

 Ⓑ cidr

 Ⓒ cidder

 Ⓓ sidr

13. The word *diner* is an example of which type of word?

 Ⓐ contraction

 Ⓑ compound word

 Ⓒ closed-syllable word

 Ⓓ open-syllable word

Name _____

Student Evaluation Chart

TESTED SKILLS	Number Correct	Percent Correct
Vocabulary	/5	%
Context clues, 1, 2, 4		
Word families, 3		
Compound words, 5		
Reading Comprehension	/4	%
Cause and effect, 6, 7		
Summarize: sequence, 8, 9		
Phonics	/4	%
Variant vowels (oo, ou), 10		
Latin roots, 11		
Open syllables: long vowels, 12, 13		
Total Weekly Test Score	/13	%

ANSWER KEY
1. C; 2. C; 3. B; 4. A; 5. D; 6. C; 7. C; 8. C; 9. A; 10. B; 11. C; 12. A; 13. D

Ike and May Fly to Help

Ike's mom is a pilot. Her name is May. She flies her own plane to places where people need help. Her crew takes food, water, and other things to places of danger.

Ike made a design of a plane. The design shows how the plane is put together. His mom said, "Ike, I think that's very good. Can you draw pictures of me and your dad?" Ike drew his mom and dad. Then he drew his cat and dog.

Then news came of a fire. "We will go soon," said May. "School is out, Ike. Do you want to come?" said May. "Yes," said Ike. The plane's crew came soon. May took off quickly. The plane flew smoothly. Ike took a notebook. He drew what he saw. He drew the fire. It was hard to breathe near the fire. He drew the crew with food for the people. He drew his mother as she flew the plane. Soon he had a book about the trip.

When Ike grew up, he wrote books. They were kids' books. They were about planes and jobs of danger. One book was about May and her plane. Ike drew art to go with the books.

© Macmillan/McGraw-Hill

Name _____

Directions: Fill in the circle next to the best answer.

1. **What does the word *crew* mean in the sentence?**

   > The *crew* loaded food and water into the plane.

   Ⓐ teachers

   Ⓑ workers

   Ⓒ passengers

   Ⓓ writers

2. **What does the word *pilot* mean in the story?**

   Ⓐ person who clears a runway

   Ⓑ person who controls air traffic

   Ⓒ person who cleans a plane

   Ⓓ person who flies a plane

3. **Rewrite the phrase: <u>the crew of a plane?</u>**

   Ⓐ the planes' crew

   Ⓑ the crew's plane

   Ⓒ the plane's crew

   Ⓓ the planes' crews

4. **Which of these is a statement of fact?**

   Ⓐ May was a good pilot.

   Ⓑ May flew her own plane.

   Ⓒ Ike's books were well written.

   Ⓓ "Ike, I think that's very good."

5. **Which of these is a statement of opinion?**

   Ⓐ May's crew was the best in the business.

   Ⓑ Ike drew his mother as she flew the plane.

   Ⓒ May flew to help people in danger.

   Ⓓ Ike drew the fire and the crew.

6. **Which word is spelled correctly?**

   Ⓐ drou

   Ⓑ dru

   Ⓒ drew

   Ⓓ drouw

7. **Choose the word that completes the sentence.**

May _____ over the fire and landed.

   Ⓐ grew

   Ⓑ flew

   Ⓒ brew

   Ⓓ crew

8. **Which word tells how the plane flew?**

   Ⓐ smoothly

   Ⓑ smooth

   Ⓒ smoothness

   Ⓓ smoothest

Name _____

Student Evaluation Chart

TESTED SKILLS	Number Correct	Percent Correct
Vocabulary	/3	%
Context clues, 1, 2		
Possessives, 3		
Reading Comprehension	/2	%
Fact and opinion, 4, 5		
Phonics	/3	%
Variant vowel (oo, ew), 6, 7		
Suffix -ly, 8		
Total Weekly Test Score	/8	%

ANSWER KEY
1. B; 2. D; 3. C; 4. B; 5. A; 6. C; 7. B; 8. A

Roy Helps Save the Soil

The village people were sad. All the soil in their fields blew away. They could not grow crops. The land was as flat as a pancake.

Joy was a farmer. She called a soil expert. His name was Roy. He gave farmers help in protecting their soil. Joy and the people in the village sat down. They listened to Roy. He said he had good news for them. They could help their soil. He gave them hope.

Roy said, "First, grow different crops each year. Do not let the soil wear out. The same crop all the time will destroy the soil."

A farmer stood up. He was full of sadness. "But we sell lots of corn. We have no choice."

Roy said, "Plant the corn in a different field. Plant something new in the corn field."

The farmers joined one another. They worked together. They were guided by Joy in their work. Joy had a strong voice in the village.

Soon the soil and the crops were better. Birds flew over the village again. The people were full of happiness. Their faces were as bright as the sun.

Name _____

Directions: Fill in the circle next to the best answer.

1. **What is the meaning of the word *soil* in the sentence?**

   All the *soil* in the fields blew away.

   Ⓐ animals and birds
   Ⓑ top layer of earth
   Ⓒ buildings
   Ⓓ tractors

2. **What is the meaning of the word *guided* in the sentence?**

   Joy took charge and *guided* them in their work.

   Ⓐ led
   Ⓑ angered
   Ⓒ paid
   Ⓓ hired

3. **Which sentence compares two unlike things?**
   Ⓐ Joy had a strong voice in the village.
   Ⓑ Do not let the soil wear out.
   Ⓒ Plant the corn in a different field.
   Ⓓ Their faces were as bright as the sun.

4. **What do you predict the people of the village will do next?**
   Ⓐ They will go back to their old ways.
   Ⓑ They will use the new ways of planting.
   Ⓒ They will leave their land and move to the city.
   Ⓓ They will grow only corn because it sells well.

Name _____

5. **What do you predict that Roy will do next?**

Ⓐ He will write a book on farming and retire.

Ⓑ He will buy a farm of his own.

Ⓒ He will stay and live in the village.

Ⓓ He will go teach farmers somewhere else.

6. **Which word is spelled correctly?**

Ⓐ voice

Ⓑ vois

Ⓒ voise

Ⓓ voic

7. **Which word completes the sentence?**

> Roy taught the farmers not to _____ their fields.

Ⓐ destroi

Ⓑ destroy

Ⓒ distroy

Ⓓ destroye

8. **Which word completes the sentence?**

> The farmers were full of _____ when their soil blew away.

Ⓐ sadnes

Ⓑ sadniss

Ⓒ sadness

Ⓓ saddness

Name _____

Student Evaluation Chart

TESTED SKILLS	Number Correct	Percent Correct
Vocabulary	/3	%
Context clues, 1, 2		
Figurative language, 3		
Reading Comprehension	/2	%
Make predictions, 4, 5		
Phonics	/2	%
Diphthong (oi, oy), 6, 7		
Structural Analysis	/1	%
Suffix -ness, 8		
Total Weekly Test Score	/8	%

ANSWER KEY
1. B; 2. A; 3. D; 4. B; 5. D; 6. A; 7. B; 8. C

The Lake in Late Winter

Mike and June stood on the edge of the frozen lake. They listened to the loud sound of cracking ice. The lake was shiny. "Look," said June. "The cracks make designs in the ice. Wow, it is chilly!"

A brook ran into the lake. It was frozen, too. "Birds and other animals are strong," said June. "Many are able to survive in the cold." She watched a crew of men. They skied through the woods. A boy drew some birds in a notebook. Some geese flew down nearby.

Soon the ice would melt. Geese and other birds could feed. The woods would have new plants for animals to eat. "The lake and the woods are important to animals," said Mike. "They are like towns are to people. Animals can find basic food, water, and shelter in the woods."

"It is impossible to skate now," said June. "The ice is too thin." She looked at the distant town. "We came a long way," she said.

Soon Mike and June were cold. "My feet are like cold stones," said June. "Let's go home. Mom will have cocoa."

Name _____

Directions: Fill in the circle next to the best answer.

1. **What does the word *impossible* mean in the passage?**

   > "It is *impossible* to skate now," said June. "The ice is too thin."

   Ⓐ very possible

   Ⓑ always possible

   Ⓒ not possible

   Ⓓ possible soon

2. **What does the word *distant* mean in the passage?**

   > June looked at the *distant* town. "We came a long way," she said.

   Ⓐ close by

   Ⓑ snowy

   Ⓒ far away

   Ⓓ huge

3. **Which word completes the sentence?**

   > The cracking ice made _____ on the surface.

   Ⓐ designs

   Ⓑ skates

   Ⓒ birds

   Ⓓ towns

© Macmillan/McGraw-Hill

4. Which word completes the sentence?

> The lake and the woods are _____ to animals.

Ⓐ impossible

Ⓑ important

Ⓒ distant

Ⓓ cracking

5. What does the word *survive* mean in the passage?

> Strong birds and animals can *survive* in the cold.

Ⓐ fly

Ⓑ swim

Ⓒ skate

Ⓓ live

6. Which sentence is an example of description?

Ⓐ June's feet were like cold stones.

Ⓑ Birds could have babies when the ice was gone.

Ⓒ Let's go home.

Ⓓ They stood on the edge of the frozen lake.

© Macmillan/McGraw-Hill

7. **Which example gives information about the sentence below?**

> "The woods are important to animals," said Mike.

  Ⓐ June's feet were cold.

  Ⓑ Animals can find food and water.

  Ⓒ The ice was too thin to skate.

  Ⓓ Many animals survive the cold.

8. **What do you predict will happen if June and Mike skate on the ice?**

  Ⓐ They will get very cold.

  Ⓑ They will race across the lake.

  Ⓒ The ice will crack.

  Ⓓ They will scare the geese.

9. **What causes June to want to go home and have cocoa?**

  Ⓐ She is hungry.

  Ⓑ She is tired.

  Ⓒ She is thirsty.

  Ⓓ She is cold.

10. **Which word completes the sentence?**

> June and Mike heard the _____ of cracking ice.

  Ⓐ sound

  Ⓑ ground

  Ⓒ news

  Ⓓ brook

11. Which word is spelled correctly?

Ⓐ chillie

Ⓑ chily

Ⓒ chilly

Ⓓ chilye

12. Which word completes the sentence?

A boy watched a bird and _____ a picture.

Ⓐ blew

Ⓑ drew

Ⓒ crew

Ⓓ grew

13. Which word is spelled correctly?

Ⓐ stude

Ⓑ stood

Ⓒ stode

Ⓓ stoud

Grade 3 • Unit 5 • Week 5

Student Evaluation Chart

TESTED SKILLS	Number Correct	Percent Correct
Vocabulary	/5	%
Context clues, 1, 2, 3, 4, 5		
Comprehension	/4	%
Description, 6, 7		
Make predictions, 8		
Cause and effect, 9		
Phonics	/3	%
Diphthong ow, ou, 10		
Variant vowel ew, 12		
Variant vowel oo, 13		
Structural Analysis	/1	
Suffix -y, 11		
Total Weekly Test Score	/13	%

ANSWER KEY
1. C; 2. C; 3. A; 4. B; 5. D; 6. D; 7. B; 8. C; 9. D; 10 A; 11. C; 12. B; 13. B

Wash Day Blues

"I can't keep track of the laundry," said Walt. "I don't know what belongs to you or me."

Paul was thoughtful. "It's not your fault. We need a better system," he said.

"I found this shirt in the hallway. Is it yours?" asked Walt.

"I wore it to school," Paul recalled. "Then I took it off when I got home," he said.

"I wore one just like it," said Walt. "I also changed when I came home. I left my shirt in the hallway, too."

"Here is a way we can keep track," said Paul. "I will just wear clothes that are red. You can just wear things that are blue."

Walt agreed to try the new system. He washed his own clothes and his brother's clothes too. "We still have a small problem," Walt told Paul. "I put your red clothes in the laundry. I put my blue clothes in, too. Now the laundry is all purple."

Paul was thoughtful. "Maybe we need a new system," he said.

Name _____

Directions: Fill in the circle next to the best answer.

1. **What does *system* mean in the sentence below?**

We need a new *system*.

   Ⓐ group of friends

   Ⓑ kind of soap

   Ⓒ way of doing things

   Ⓓ girl in our family

2. **Use story clues to choose the meaning.**

Laundry is _____.

   Ⓐ clothing that you throw away

   Ⓑ clothing that you wash

   Ⓒ clothing that is red

   Ⓓ clothing that is blue

3. **Use story clues to choose the meaning.**

When Paul *recalled* something, he _____.

   Ⓐ changed his mind

   Ⓑ changed his clothes

   Ⓒ remembered what he did

   Ⓓ did the laundry

4. **Which sentence tells the lesson of the story?**

   Ⓐ If things don't work out, try something else.

   Ⓑ Friends will always be with you in hard times.

   Ⓒ Don't waste anything, and you won't need anything.

   Ⓓ You should clean up after others.

5. **How do the brothers work together?**

   Ⓐ They agree to share their clothes.

   Ⓑ They promise to put their clothes away.

   Ⓒ They take turns doing the laundry.

   Ⓓ They try to make a plan that will work.

6. **It's not your _____ .**

   Ⓐ fault

   Ⓑ fallt

   Ⓒ fauled

   Ⓓ fawlt

7. **What does the word part -*ful* mean in the word *thoughtful*?**

   Ⓐ thought again

   Ⓑ full of thought

   Ⓒ not thought

   Ⓓ able to think

8. **How do worms _____ if they don't have legs?**

   Ⓐ craull

   Ⓑ croll

   Ⓒ crawel

   Ⓓ crawl

Grade 3 • Unit 6 • Week 1

Student Evaluation Chart

TESTED SKILLS	Number Correct	Percent Correct
Vocabulary	/3	%
Paragraph clues, 1, 2, 3		
Reading Comprehension	/2	%
Theme, 4, 5		
Phonics	/3	%
Variant vowel (au, aw, al), 6, 8		
Prefixes and suffixes, 7		
Total Weekly Test Score	/8	%

ANSWER KEY
1. C; 2. B; 3. C; 4. A; 5. D; 6. A; 7. B; 8. D

The Picnic

Chip planned a picnic yesterday. "I'd better check the weather report," he said. Chip was certain the day would be nice. Still, he turned on the news. It said the day would be partly sunny. Chip stopped paying attention.

Today at dawn, Chip prowled around the kitchen. He was looking for a basket. Chip packed his lunch in the basket. Something was bothering Chip. He was certain he forgot to pack something. But he could not remember what it was.

Chip rode off to the park. Then he spread out his lunch under a tree. Soon the sky began to change. A couple of big, dark clouds came by. The weather started to change. Soon it began to sprinkle. *Splash*! Chip put the basket over his head. *Splash*! The rain came right through onto Chip's head. He was unable to enjoy his lunch.

Chip recalled, "The TV said partly sunny. Then I didn't pay attention. It must have said partly rainy, too. I forgot to pack an umbrella!"

Name _____

Directions: Fill in the circle next to the best answer.

1. **What does *yesterday* mean in the sentence below?**

   Yesterday, Chip planned a picnic.

   Ⓐ the day after today

   Ⓑ right now

   Ⓒ one day next week

   Ⓓ the day before today

2. **Chip should have been paying _____.**

   Ⓐ picnic

   Ⓑ sprinkle

   Ⓒ couple

   Ⓓ attention

3. **What does *certain* mean in the sentence below?**

   He was *certain* he forgot to pack something.

   Ⓐ afraid

   Ⓑ sure

   Ⓒ careless

   Ⓓ hungry

4. **In the word *remake*, the word part *re-* means ____.**

   Ⓐ full of make

   Ⓑ make again

   Ⓒ able to make

   Ⓓ not make

Name _____

5. What does *change* mean in the sentence below?

> Soon the sky began to *change*.

   Ⓐ look different

   Ⓑ get bright

   Ⓒ put on something else

   Ⓓ give money

6. Which word best describes how Chip felt when it began to rain?

   Ⓐ foolish

   Ⓑ sleepy

   Ⓒ happy

   Ⓓ angry

7. What judgment can you make at the end of the story?

   Ⓐ Chip will invite a friend next time.

   Ⓑ Chip cannot wait to have another picnic.

   Ⓒ Chip knows he should pay attention next time.

   Ⓓ Chip will not bring a basket to the next picnic.

© Macmillan/McGraw-Hill

Name _____

8. **What lesson does the story teach?**

   Ⓐ Paying attention can keep you from having problems.

   Ⓑ Don't go on a picnic by yourself.

   Ⓒ Use a basket when you forget your umbrella.

   Ⓓ The park is not a good place for a picnic.

9. **What will Chip probably do next time?**

   Ⓐ Forget to pack his umbrella.

   Ⓑ Pay attention to all of the weather report.

   Ⓒ Pack his lunch in an umbrella.

   Ⓓ Look and listen with care.

10. **Soon it began to _____ .**

    Ⓐ sprinkel

    Ⓑ srinkle

    Ⓒ spinkle

    Ⓓ sprinkle

Name _____

11. Which word has an ending that means it happened in the past?

Ⓐ bothering

Ⓑ paying

Ⓒ planned

Ⓓ looks

12. Which word has a prefix that means *not*?

Ⓐ prowled

Ⓑ remember

Ⓒ unable

Ⓓ packed

13. Chip woke up at _____ .

Ⓐ donn

Ⓑ dawn

Ⓒ daun

Ⓓ doun

Name _____

Student Evaluation Chart

TESTED SKILLS	Number Correct	Percent Correct
Vocabulary	/5	%
Context clues, 1, 2, 3, 5		
Prefixes and suffixes, 4		
Reading Comprehension	/4	%
Make judgments, 6, 7		
Theme, 8, 9		
Phonics	/2	%
Constant blends and digraphs, 10		
Variant Vowel (au, aw, al), 13		
Structural Analysis	/2	%
Inflectional endings, 11		
Prefixes and suffixes, 12		
Total Weekly Test Score	/13	%

ANSWER KEY
1. D; 2. D; 3. B; 4. B; 5. A; 6. A; 7. C; 8. A; 9. D; 10. D; 11. C; 12. C; 13. B

Fast in Space, Slow Below

The brave astronaut boarded the space shuttle. The trip might frighten many people. Not her. She was unafraid.

She was in no hurry for daylight to arrive. She loved being up in the dark, quiet sky. Late at night, she could see many lands below. There was Africa, right below her. It was fun to exercise in the shuttle, too. She could fly free as a bird.

Back on the ground, many people were going to work. Some took a train. Some drove cars in busy places. Many people were unhappy. Their ride was long and slow. The cars and trains stopped many times. The people would arrive late for work.

Some people wondered, "Science can get people to the moon. Why can't it make it easier to get to work here on Earth?

© Macmillan/McGraw-Hill

Name _____

Directions: Fill in the circle next to the best answer.

1. **What does *exercise* mean in the sentence below?**

   It was fun to <u>exercise</u> in the shuttle.

   Ⓐ move your body around

   Ⓑ look out the window

   Ⓒ eat dinner

   Ⓓ take a nap

2. **A <u>brave</u> person is**

   Ⓐ often late.

   Ⓑ not afraid.

   Ⓒ not hungry.

   Ⓓ quite friendly.

3. **An <u>astronaut</u> is a person who**

   Ⓐ walks to work.

   Ⓑ travels in space.

   Ⓒ takes the train.

   Ⓓ drives a car.

4. **Who has a problem in this story?**

   Ⓐ the astronaut in the shuttle

   Ⓑ people who look at the stars

   Ⓒ people who take cars or trains to work

   Ⓓ people who study science

5. **What problem does the story tell about?**

   Ⓐ having cars that break down

   Ⓑ going to Africa

   Ⓒ traveling in space

   Ⓓ getting to work by car or train

6. **We hope the _____ will come on time.**

   Ⓐ trane

   Ⓑ trayn

   Ⓒ train

   Ⓓ tran

7. **Which word is spelled correctly?**

   Ⓐ daylight

   Ⓑ daylite

   Ⓒ daylyte

   Ⓓ dayliet

8. **We were _____ that the movie started before we arrived.**

   Ⓐ onhappy

   Ⓑ unnhappy

   Ⓒ inhappy

   Ⓓ unhappy

Grade 3 • Unit 6 • Week 3

Student Evaluation Chart

TESTED SKILLS	Number Correct	Percent Correct
Vocabulary	/3	%
Context clues, 1, 2		
Greek roots, 3		
Reading Comprehension	/2	%
Problem and Solution, 4, 5		
Phonics	/2	%
Long a (ay, ai), 6		
Long i (i, igh, ie, y), 7		
Structural Analysis	/1	%
Prefixes and Suffixes, 8		
Total Weekly Test Score	/8	%

ANSWER KEY
1. A; 2. B; 3. B; 4. C; 5. D; 6. C; 7. A; 8. D

No Place to Play

Joe was sweeping the sidewalk in front of his house. There was nothing else for him to do. He had no place to play with his friends. His home was too small. The street was not safe.

Joe's broom swept up something strange. He had to stoop to pick up the paper. Joe quickly read the information. It was a notice about a meeting. The purpose of the meeting was to hear a speech. The mayor would talk about building a new playground. Joe rushed in to show his mother the notice.

"That's strange," said his mother. "I had a dream just last night. I dreamed there was a good place for you to play close to our home. I think I will go to the meeting. Maybe my dream will come true."

Name _____

Directions: Fill in the circle next to the best answer.

1. **What does *strange* mean in the sentence below?**

   Joe's broom swept up something <u>strange</u>.

   Ⓐ dirty

   Ⓑ funny

   Ⓒ odd

   Ⓓ powerful

2. **When you need *information*, you want**

   Ⓐ a playground.

   Ⓑ a friend.

   Ⓒ details.

   Ⓓ food.

3. **The ending *-ly* on the word *quickly* means**

   Ⓐ in a way.

   Ⓑ more.

   Ⓒ not.

   Ⓓ full of.

4. **What is the writer's main purpose for writing this story?**

   Ⓐ to entertain readers with a fun story

   Ⓑ to inform readers about a town meeting

   Ⓒ to show readers how children use playgrounds

   Ⓓ to persuade readers to sweep sidewalks

5. **What was the main purpose for writing the notice that Joe found?**

   Ⓐ to make readers laugh

   Ⓑ to inform readers about a meeting

   Ⓒ to teach people how to build a playground

   Ⓓ to persuade people to keep their yards neat

6. **Pat will _____ the ball to you.**

   Ⓐ throa

   Ⓑ throe

   Ⓒ throuw

   Ⓓ throw

7. **Did you listen to the _____?**

   Ⓐ speach

   Ⓑ speche

   Ⓒ spech

   Ⓓ speech

8. **Choose the word with the correct syllable breaks.**

   Ⓐ in/forma/tion

   Ⓑ in/for/ma/tion

   Ⓒ in/for/mat/ion

   Ⓓ inf/or/mat/ion

Name _____

Grade 3 • Unit 6 • Week 4

Student Evaluation Chart

TESTED SKILLS	Number Correct	Percent Correct
Vocabulary	/3	%
Context clues, 1, 2		
Suffixes, 3		
Reading Comprehension	/2	%
Author's purpose, 4, 5		
Phonics	/3	%
Long o (oa, ow, oe), 6		
Long e (ee, ea, ey, y), 7		
Multisyllable words, 8		
Total Weekly Test Score	/8	%

ANSWER KEY
1. C; 2. C; 3. A; 4. A; 5. B; 6. D; 7. D; 8. B

The Clown that Frowned

"Clowns scare me," said Ruth.

"Why?" asked her friend Judy.

Ruth said, "I went to the circus. It had three clowns. The biggest one wore a frown the whole time. The clown pretended he was going to exercise with a ball. The adults at the circus all laughed. Then the clown threw the ball to me," Ruth recalled. "I was scared. I tried to shrink under my seat when he came near me," she said. "I was certain he was going to do something mean!"

Judy was thoughtful. Then she said, "Clowns show simple emotions. That clown wasn't mean. He was supposed to look sad. That frown was painted on! Maybe if you played with him, you could have turned his frown upside down."

Name _____

Directions: Fill in the circle next to the best answer.

1. **What does *shrink* mean in the sentence below?**

   I tried to *shrink* under my seat when he came near me.

   Ⓐ make clothing get smaller
   Ⓑ move away in fear
   Ⓒ play with a ball
   Ⓓ say something out loud

2. **What does *emotions* mean in the sentence below?**

   Clowns show simple *emotions*.

   Ⓐ tricks
   Ⓑ faces
   Ⓒ feelings
   Ⓓ balloons

3. **An *adult* is a person who is**
   Ⓐ funny to watch.
   Ⓑ very young.
   Ⓒ a good friend.
   Ⓓ a grownup.

4. **Which word means "not sure"?**

Ⓐ thought

Ⓑ certain

Ⓒ thoughtful

Ⓓ uncertain

5. **Which word means "remembered"?**

Ⓐ recalled

Ⓑ laughed

Ⓒ pretended

Ⓓ said

6. **Judy said Ruth could have turned the clown's frown upside down. What did Judy mean?**

Ⓐ Ruth could trick the clown.

Ⓑ Ruth could stand on her head.

Ⓒ Ruth could make the clown smile.

Ⓓ Ruth could paint a new face on the clown.

7. **Why did the clown probably wear a frown?**

Ⓐ to make people scared

Ⓑ to make people cry

Ⓒ to pretend he was sad

Ⓓ to pretend he was mean

© Macmillan/McGraw-Hill

8. **What is the writer's purpose for writing this story?**

   Ⓐ to entertain readers with an interesting story

   Ⓑ to persuade readers that clowns are mean

   Ⓒ to inform readers about how clowns paint their faces

   Ⓓ to teach readers that circuses are scary

9. **What was Ruth's problem?**

   Ⓐ She did not want to exercise.

   Ⓑ She was afraid of the clown.

   Ⓒ She did not like to play catch.

   Ⓓ She did not want to be teased.

10. **I tried to catch the ball when she _____ it.**

   Ⓐ threw

   Ⓑ thraw

   Ⓒ throu

   Ⓓ throo

Name _____

11. **Some people always smile and some people always**

Ⓐ froun.

Ⓑ froughn.

Ⓒ fraun.

Ⓓ frown.

12. **Ruth ate _____ pizza at the circus.**

Ⓐ chease

Ⓑ chees

Ⓒ cheese

Ⓓ ceese

13. **Don't be _____ of clowns.**

Ⓐ afraid.

Ⓑ afriad.

Ⓒ afrad.

Ⓓ afread.

Grade 3 • Unit 6 • Week 5

Student Evaluation Chart

TESTED SKILLS	Number Correct	Percent Correct
Vocabulary	/5	%
Multiple-meaning words, 1		
Context clues, 2, 3		
Prefixes, 4, 5		
Reading Comprehension	/4	%
Draw conclusions, 6, 7		
Author's purpose, 8		
Problem and solution, 9		
Phonics	/4	%
Variant Vowels (oo, ew; oo, ou; au, aw, al), 10		
Diphthong (ou, ow), 11		
Long e (ee, ea, ey, y), 12		
Long a (ay, ai), 13		
Total Weekly Test Score	/13	%

ANSWER KEY
1. B; 2. C; 3. D; 4. D; 5. A; 6. C; 7. C; 8. A; 9. B; 10.A; 11. D; 12. C; 13. A